DESIGN in the Making

textiles
technology

Longman

Steve Cushing

Contents

Introduction

Textiles

This book has been written to support your Design and Technology work in textile products. The word textiles is used to describe any product that is made from fabric. The word itself comes from the Latin word *texere*, which means to weave. It was probably the weather that forced our ancestors to make the first textile products. When you're cold and wet, you cover your body. Our prehistoric ancestors used animal skins, leaves and the bark of trees to cover themselves and so keep warm and dry. The leaves will not have lasted very long and the animal skins were very heavy.

As the raw materials were the wrong shape and size, people needed to join them together. They invented different ways of doing this using thorns and bone. As one method of joining the material together led to another, the first bone needle was invented. Our ancestors sewed together the animal skins and raw material using hair and sinew.

It wasn't long before beads and shells were added, not for warmth but for decoration. The stitching itself was also used for decoration. This gave rise to binding, borders and embroidered surface patterns. The use of textile products purely to cover the body had changed. Fashion had begun. Gradually our ancestors learnt how to collect the hairs from animal skins and twist them together to make yarn. Yarn could then be made into fabric and the fabric into textile products. This will be explored in more detail in Section Two. Clothes made of fabric are much more comfortable than clothes made from skins.

As people discovered new ways to decorate their clothes, embroidery and decoration became an important part of life. Every garment was individual and hand made. As time passed two types of embroidery developed, one called **greater** and the other called **folk**.

Embroidery for garments made to be worn became known as folk embroidery. The designs were generally traditional and related specifically to the culture of the maker. Great embroidery was produced for churches, governments, the military and rich landowners.

Today, textile products remain a very important part of our lives. We use them as clothing to protect us and for decoration on our bodies and in our homes. Developments in textile technology have narrowed the gap between art, design, engineering and science. The use of flexible materials is increasing daily. Design and Technology is about developing ideas for things you can make and having the knowledge, skills and understanding to make your ideas into products. This book focuses on designing and making with flexible materials.

Design and Technology is a practical subject and should be fun. It is by making things that we gain many of the skills we need to design and make new products. But it is also important that we understand the theoretical knowledge that underpins any Design and Technology activity.

This book contains some of the theoretical knowledge you will need to be able to design and make quality textile products. But you need to learn by doing, not just reading about Design and Technology. Different people learn in different ways. The book focuses on both practical skills and knowledge to allow you to use your design ability and to use correct procedures and processes. The book has been written, not as a course, but as a reference point and to reinforce your teacher's practical demonstrations. Without underpinning knowledge and good making skills, designed products lack real quality.

All of the photographs and pictures are of Key Stage 3 pupils' work. The process photographs are also of Key Stage 3 pupils using their hands and relevant machines to produce their practical outcomes.

The book contains suggestions for practical tasks: your teacher will guide you and tell you which sections of the book you should be working from. In other words, this book will be used as a resource and you will dip into it to find the necessary knowledge and skills to support the course your teacher has developed for you. Although the book has been developed for Key Stage 3, the knowledge and skills it contains are also an extremely useful resource for students undertaking GCSE courses at Key Stage 4.

Designing and making

Designing cannot be separated from making. This means that when you are designing you should be thinking about how your product could be made, and when you are making you should be thinking about how your textile product could be better designed. It is not possible to design anything without some practical knowledge of materials and the making skills needed to turn them into something useful.

You should not see designing as something you do prior to making and then forget about. When making products, you should also be thinking about changes that could be made to improve your product and about how you would modify your design if you made the product again.

Your teacher will use some activities to help you to learn the skills needed to produce good-quality outcomes. This may include product disassembly: you look at existing products and what they are made of. Some practical activities are aimed at giving you an opportunity to practise new skills, concepts and procedures. Other activities will enable you to put your knowledge, skills and understanding to effective use. The best way to learn is to put your knowledge and skills to the test. Don't be afraid to ask for help.

Using Information and Communications Technology (ICT)

Wherever possible you should use ICT to enhance your Design and Technology work. You can use ICT to draft out your ideas; it allows you to draft and redraft work, a vital process in Design and Technology. ICT also helps you to present your work in an orderly and effective way. CD-ROMs and the Internet provide a valuable source of information relating to Design and Technology.

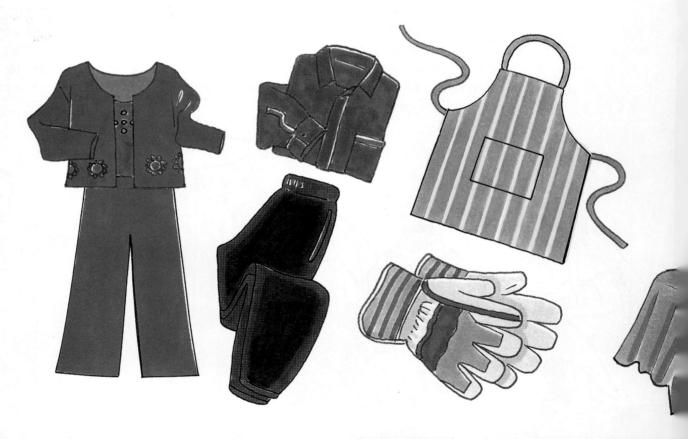

What you will be doing

We use textiles every day, in all sorts of ways. For example, window curtains are used to keep out draughts, shut out the light and stop people staring into our homes; shower curtains are used to keep the bathroom floor dry.

A wide range of textiles are used for specialised purposes, such as in hospitals, the workplace, and for sports. Even heart valves are made from textiles. New fabrics are being invented all the time. They are used in the fashion industry, and to make textile products that improve our lives. In considering a type of fabric for a particular use, designers need to think about its **properties**. This might mean asking 'is it waterproof?' or 'is it heat resistant?'

As you work through the book you will be learning about making things with tools and equipment. You will learn about health and safety and will acquire the skills and knowledge needed to design your own products. This book will help you to learn these skills with the help of your teacher or parent.

Activity 1

We use textiles in the home for clothing, furniture and decoration. Collect a range of pictures from catalogues and magazines to show different uses of textile products.

Under the headings **clothing**, **furniture**, and **decoration** collect a range of pictures from catalogues and magazines to show different uses of textile products. For each product state its purpose and say how well it meets this purpose.

We use textiles to provide protection from the weather, as in the case of protective clothing, and for decoration, as in the case of fashion clothing. Sometimes textile products achieve both protection and decoration. Collect a range of pictures from catalogues and magazines to show different uses of textile products. Under the headings **protection** and **decoration** make a list of textile products. Try to choose items from your home that fit into one or other of the categories: for example, an oven glove is used to provide protection, while a wall hanging is for decoration. For each product state its purpose and say how well it meets this purpose.

Tools and Equipment

When designing and making textile products you will use a wide variety of tools and equipment. You need to learn how to use this equipment in order to produce quality products safely.

Safety

Safety and using tools

Many of the tools you use in the textiles workshop have sharp edges. If you take care they will help you to produce high-quality work. If you handle them incorrectly they may cause damage and spoil your work.

Fabric dyes and inks are chemicals. If the chemicals are handled correctly they are safe and harmless. If you do not follow the correct instructions and wear the correct protective clothing, they are dangerous. You should always keep the workshop clean and tidy.

Safety rules

Safety rules are simple:
- Always carry sharp tools with the sharp edge pointing downwards.
- Never run around in the workshop.
- Do not obstruct the floor or worktops.
- Wear an overall to protect your clothes.
- Roll up long sleeves and tuck in ties and loose clothing when using machines.
- Tie back long hair.
- Wear gloves and special clothing when necessary.
- Know the safety drill –e.g. how to switch off the machines.
- Always tell your teacher immediately if you have an accident.
- See your doctor if you have an allergic reaction to any of the fabric dyes and chemicals.

The textiles workshop contains danger from many sources. You should always check possible risks with your teacher and make sure that you wear the right protective clothing.

Danger from liquids
- Spray and mist from liquids can affect your breathing and hurt your eyes.
- Some liquids are toxic and can burn your clothing and skin.
- Vapours from the evaporation of liquids can be poisonous.
- Gas from liquids can be explosive.
- Textile chemicals used for dying can cause allergic reactions.

Danger from solids
- Dust from cutting can affect your breathing and hurt your eyes.
- Smoke from burning or heating solids can be poisonous.
- Fumes from burning fabrics can be poisonous.

Activity 2

Look around the textiles room to see how it is organised. Think about safety:
Where are the electric sockets?
Where are the irons stored?
Are sharp items like scissors and needles stored appropriately?

Activity 3

Tools, machines and chemicals can be very dangerous unless you follow the correct procedures for using them. You must always observe safety rules in the school workshop. The rules refer to your dress, your actions and your use of machines. Draw up a list of safety points for the school textile workshop. Add pictures to your list if you like.

Tools, machines and chemicals can be very dangerous if you do not use them correctly. You must always observe safety rules. These rules refer to your clothing, your actions and your use of machines and chemicals. Draw up two lists of safety considerations, one relating to the **type of clothing** that you should wear, and one relating to the **correct use of tools and equipment**. Design a poster to illustrate your safety considerations.

Tools, machines and chemicals can be very dangerous if used incorrectly. You must always observe safety rules. These rules refer to your use of appropriate clothing, your actions in the workshop and your use of tools, machines and chemicals. Draw up a list of safety considerations under the following headings: clothing and personal safety, use of tools, use of chemicals, use of machines. Under each heading list six safety rules. Choose one of the safety rules and design a safety poster. Your poster must be clear and simple, but effective.

Cutting Tools

Scissors

Scissors are used for cutting out thin paper to make patterns. Do not use fabric or tailor's shears to cut paper. It will spoil them. Left-handed scissors and shears are available.

Tailor's shears

Tailor's shears have large finger holes and are specially shaped to cut thick fabric.

Fabric shears

Fabric shears are used for cutting out fabric. The blades of fabric shears have smooth cutting edges. It is very important that these remain sharp. Never use fabric shears for cutting paper, as this would blunt the shears.

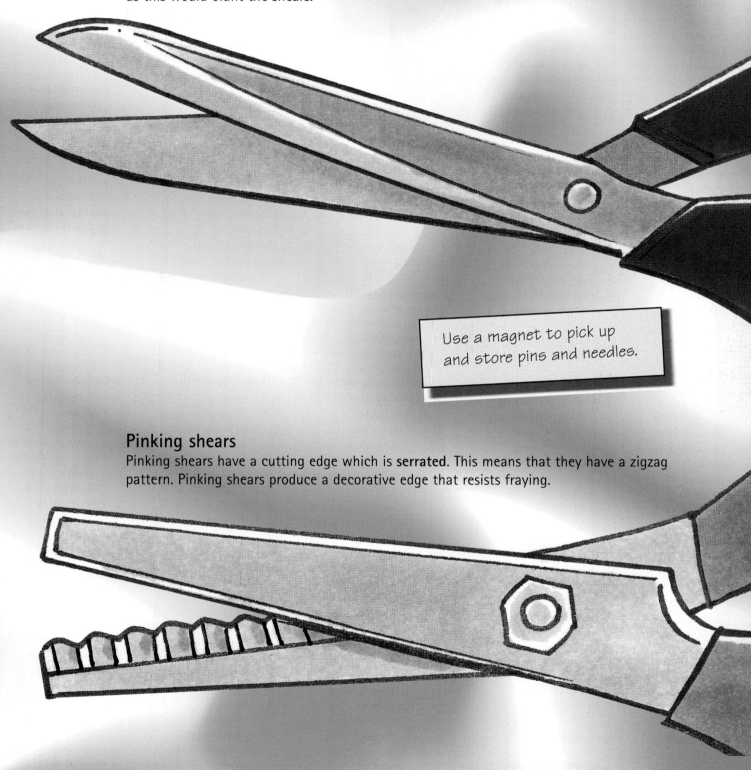

Use a magnet to pick up and store pins and needles.

Pinking shears

Pinking shears have a cutting edge which is **serrated**. This means that they have a zigzag pattern. Pinking shears produce a decorative edge that resists fraying.

Embroidery scissors

These are small scissors used for cutting the fine threads used in embroidery and hand sewing.

Needles

There are two main types of sharp needle: embroidery and sewing needles. There are also tapestry needles, which are blunt.

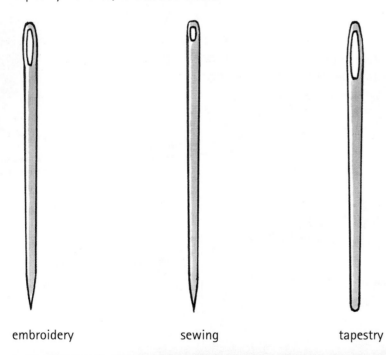

embroidery   sewing   tapestry

Needles come in a wide range of lengths and thicknesses. Which needle you use depends on the type and thickness of the yarn that you are going to use, and the thickness of the fabric.

A needle is used to punch a hole a through the fabric. The hole must be big enough to allow the yarn to pass through freely.
- Shorter needles are easier to use on thick fabric.
- Long needles are used for general sewing.
- The thickness of the needle depends on the size of the eye.

You will need to choose a needle with an eye that fits the yarn you are going to use.
- If the eye of the needle is not large enough, it will not make a big enough hole in the fabric. The yarn will cause the fabric to fray.
- If the eye of the needle is too large, it will leave a hole in the fabric.
- Some fabrics have holes between the threads that were used to make them. You do not need a sharp needle to sew fabric like this.

There are specialist needles for embroidery and darning.

Three ways to thread a needle

Always try the settings on the sewing machine on fabric scraps first.

Fold the thread over needle and then push folded end through the eye of the needle.

Fold a small piece of paper around thread and push through the eye of the needle.

Use a needle threader.

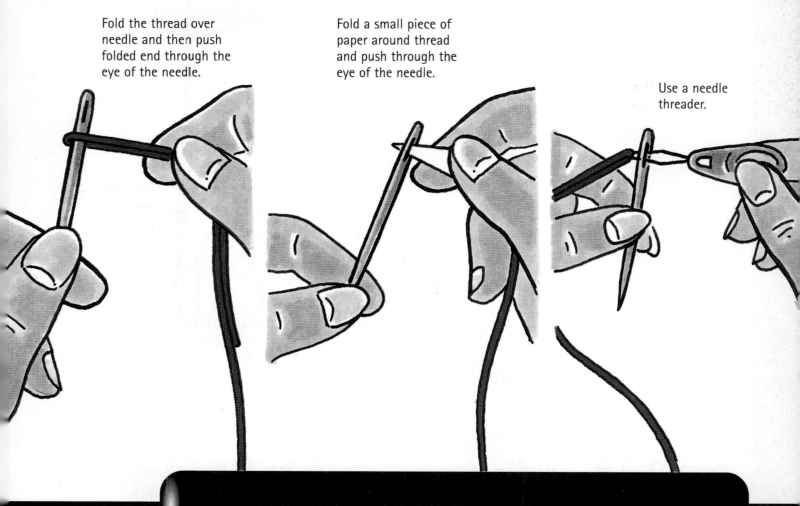

Knitting Needles

Knitting needles are used for hand knitting. They come in various sizes and lengths. In the past, knitting needles were made of wood or bone. Today they are usually made of lightweight plastics. There are specialist needles, including some with points at both ends. These are used for knitting rounds, such as sweater necks, and for knitting patterns called cables.

Stitch Ripper (quick pick)

This is used to undo stitches. Sometimes it is called a quick pick.

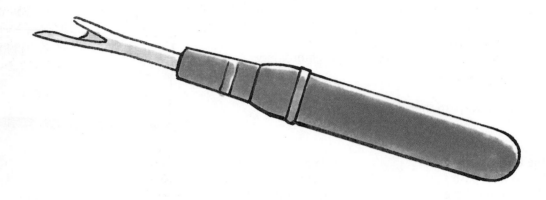

Measuring Tape

This is used to measure fabric and the body accurately.

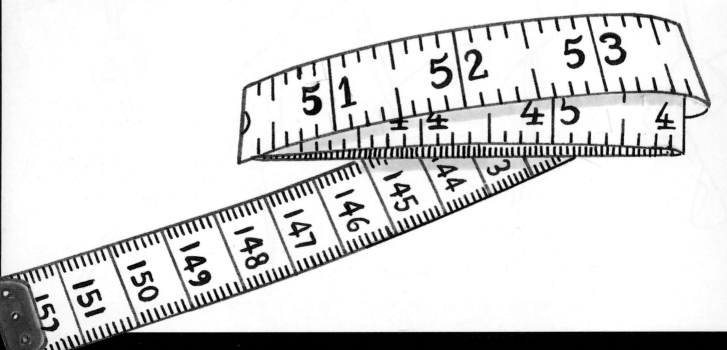

Pins

Pins come in a range of lengths and thicknesses to suit different types of fabric. Pins are important for assembling the component parts of your textile designs.

CAD/CAM

Computer-Aided Design

Computer-Aided Design is the use of a computer to design objects. Computer-Aided Design has a number of advantages over traditional methods, such as using a pencil and paper. It is like comparing handwriting and using a word processor: designs can be changed on screen; they can be saved on disk; they can be reduced or enlarged to suit different sizes; they can be cut and pasted into other designs. Modern CAD packages also allow designers to design in three dimensions. They can put their designs onto a virtual model and then rotate their designs to look at them from different angles. The computer can also fit the design onto the fabric and calculate costs.

Another advantage of new technology is that a number of designers can work on the same textile design. Since they use the Internet, these designers do not need to be in the same building. They can even be in different countries! CAD packages often generate automatically all of the drawings, and list all of the parts necessary for manufacture. Sometimes the designs are sent direct to a Computer-Aided Manufacturing machine. This is called CAD/CAM. Your school may have a computer embroidery or knitting machine that links to a design package.

Computer-Aided Manufacture

The use of computers in processing materials is called **Computer-Aided Manufacture** (CAM). Computer-Aided Manufacture involves controlling tools and machinery with computers. The computer can control exactly where the cutting tool moves to and when and where a cut is made. Computer-aided knitting machines and looms are common in the textile industry. Computer cutting machines enable textile manufacturers to produce lots of accurate pieces that are identical in shape and size. There are a large number of different types of CAM machines in industry. You may have a computer-controlled sewing or embroidery machine in school. If so, your teacher will demonstrate this machine to you.

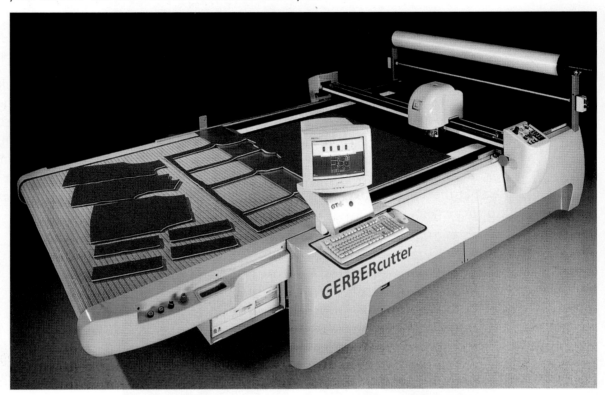

Sewing Machines

Sewing machines use two threads. One of the threads is kept in a **bobbin** held inside the machine; the other comes from a reel at the top of the machine. The needle uses both threads and forms interlocking loops. It is essential to make sure that the **tension** (tightness) of both threads is correct. By using the sewing machine controls it is also possible to change the size of the stitches.

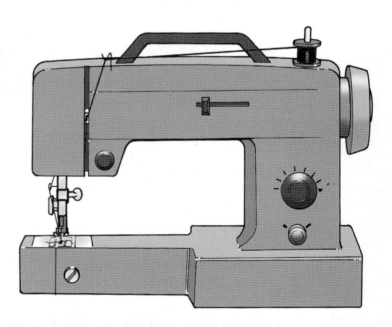

A sewing machine works by pushing a needle and top thread through the fabric whilst a spool called a bobbin rotates under the fabric. A hook on the bobbin picks up the top thread and loops it round the bottom thread. Ideally, in correct sewing, the loops between the two threads should sit between the two layers of fabric with no slack, forming an even line of stitches.

If the sewing tension is not correct, either excessive loops will be formed on the underside of the fabric being sewn, indicating that the tension is too loose, or the fabric will be scrunched up, with excessive loops on the top side, indicating that the tension is too tight. Occasionally, you might want to alter the tension on purpose to create a special fabric effect.

When using the sewing machine, you need to be careful in selecting the right size and type of needle for the fabric you are working on. Stretchy and lightweight fabrics are usually sewn with a ball-point needle. A sharp needle can cause such fabrics to ladder.

As with hand stitching, the machine can produce a wide range of stitches. Computerised and electronically controlled sewing machines often have hundreds of stitches to choose from.

Overlockers are used to produce an oversewn edge. They produce a stitch which goes over the edge of the fabric and prevents fraying or knitted fabric from coming undone.

Overlockers have up to four top threads but no bobbin.

Activity 4

Make a list of three pieces of equipment used in the textiles room. Draw each piece of equipment. For each piece of equipment state the safety rules.

Select four pieces of equipment used in the textiles room. Draw and annotate each piece of equipment to show how it should be held and used and any safety rules.

Select three pieces of equipment and one machine used in the textiles room. Draw and annotate each of your selections to show how it should be held and used and any safety rules.

Section 2

Fabrics

Making Fabric

In this section of the book you will explore common fabrics, their properties and uses. You will also learn how to make your own fabric for textile products.

There are a wide variety of fabrics in the textile products we use every day. All of these products are designed to serve a particular purpose, such as to keep us warm, to protect us from the rain or to add decoration. For the products to function properly, the fabric that the designer uses must have the right properties. These properties may range from crease resistance and a beautiful appearance through to special properties, such as elasticity and heat resistance. The fabric used to make an oven glove has different properties from those of the fabric used to make a summer blouse or shirt.

Activity 5

> Make a list of five different types of textile products found in the home. Your list should include at least one item from each of the kitchen, bedroom and bathroom. What words can you use to describe the material the product is made from? Soft, flexible, rough, smooth, thick, thin, heavy, light – make a list of words you could use. Now describe each object using your list of words.

> Make a list of six different types of textile products found in the home. Your list should include at least two items from each of the kitchen, bedroom and bathroom. What words can you use to describe the material the product is made from? Soft, flexible, rough, smooth, thick, thin, heavy, light – make a list of words you could use. Try to put the words in your list into groups, for example describing the appearance, describing the feel, describing the weight. Now describe each textile product using your list of words. If you have access to a word processor it will help you to complete this activity.

> Make a list of six different types of textile products found in the home. Your list should include at least two items from each of the kitchen, bedroom and bathroom. What words can you use to describe the material the product is made from? Soft, flexible, rough, smooth, thick, thin, heavy, light – make a list of words you could use. Try to put your wordlist into groups, for example describing the appearance, describing the feel, describing the weight. Now describe each textile product using your list of words. State why you think the material was chosen for each product. If you have access to a word processor it will help you to complete this activity.

For more on weaving see pages 27–33.
For more on knitting see pages 34–41.

Making Fibre, Yarn and Fabric

Before any textile product can be made, the **fabric** must be produced. Most designers buy their fabric ready made. They choose their fabrics carefully to have the right properties.

Fabric is made from **yarn**. Yarn is made from **fibres**. The yarn and the way the fabric is made give the fabric its properties. Before you can choose fabric with the right properties to suit the textile product you are going to make, you need to understand the properties of yarn and the methods of fabric production.

> Do not store fabric folded – a roll is better.

Fibre

The raw material used to make textile products is called fibre. Fabric can be made by **weaving, knitting** or **bonding** fibres together. You need to learn about how fibres are made first into **yarns** and then into **fabric**. Textile technology is about using yarns and fabric to make finished products.

Before the Industrial Revolution all yarns were produced by hand using a spinning wheel. Today, yarns are produced in textile mills. Although the machines that are used are different, the basic process is still the same.

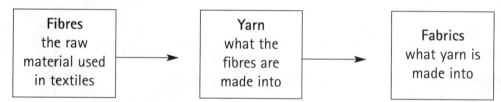

| **Fibres**
the raw material used in textiles | → | **Yarn**
what the fibres are made into | → | **Fabrics**
what yarn is made into |

So, fibres are the building blocks from which fabrics are made. Fibres are like hair and can be natural or manufactured.

Fibres have different properties. Some fibres are weak, some are strong, some are warm and some are cool. They come in many forms: thin, thick, rough, coarse, smooth, textured, transparent (see-through) and opaque (not see-through). Fibres are selected for their properties. The process of turning fibres into yarns is called **conversion**.

Natural fibres

There are two types of natural fibres: **cellulose fibres** and **protein fibres**. Natural fibres come from natural sources, that is plants and animals. Most natural fibres are very short in length. Wool and cotton are the most common natural fibres. Different breeds of sheep give wool with different lengths of fibre.

Natural fibres are also called **staple fibres**. Staple fibres must be made into yarn before they can be used.

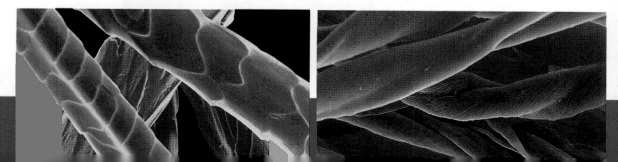

Manufactured fibres

There are two main groups of manufactured fibres: **synthetic fibres** and **made fibres**.

Synthetic fibres are made from chemicals obtained from **coal** or **petroleum**. **Nylon** was the first synthetic fibre. It was invented in 1935. PVC, elastane, polyester and acrylic are all synthetic fibres.

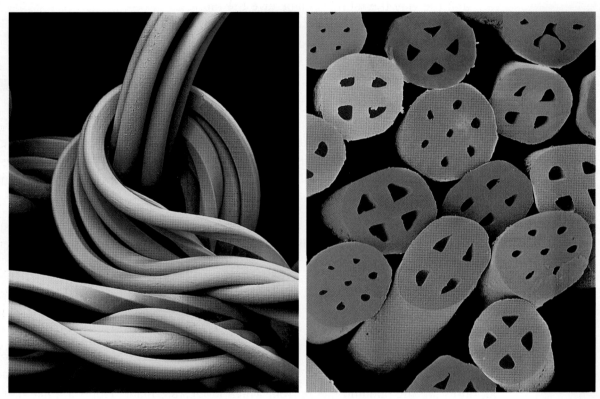

Made fibres are produced from natural and synthetic sources. They are often called regenerated fibres. **Regenerated fibres** are slightly cheaper to produce than other types of manufactured fibres because they use waste products. Cellulose from cotton and wood pulp is mixed with chemicals to change its structure into something that can be spun into yarn.

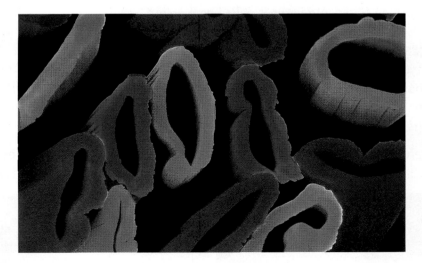

Fleece is made, in part, from recycled plastic drinks bottles.

Identifying Fibres

Most manufactured fibres are continuous lengths. These are called **filament fibres**. Silk is the only *natural* filament fibre. Filament fibres are often measured in yards. Single silk cocoons have been known to produce 3000 yards of fibre. Filament fibres can be used without being twisted together. If they are twisted together, the yarn is called a **multi-filament** yarn. Multi-filament yarn is strong, flexible and elastic. Single-filament yarns are used to make invisible threads.

You can identify a fibre by its feel and look. Remember that natural fibres are short. If it looks as if the fibre is a continuous length it must be a filament fibre or silk. If it is irregular it is probably a natural fibre. Wool has a hairy appearance, rayon a shiny appearance. Wool feels warm and soft, linen cold.

You can look at labels to see what fibres have been used. Identifying manufactured fibres can be difficult as manufacturers often give their own names for manufactured fibres. These are called brand names.

Activity 6

Look at 10 textile items in the home and find the name of the fibre on the care label. Make a list of the 10 fibres and for each one, describe its texture. What other textile items do you think this fibre could be used for?

Look at 10 textile items in the home and find the name of the fibre on the care label. Make a list of the 10 fibres and for each one, describe its texture. What other textile items do you think this fibre could be used for, and what are the properties of the fibre that makes it suitable?

Look at 10 textile items in the home and find the name of the fibre on the care label. Try to match manufactured trade names with the general name given to the fibre. Make a list of the 10 fibres and for each one, describe its texture and use. What other textile items do you think this fibre could be used for, and what properties does it have that make it suitable?

Group activity: create a spreadsheet and present the data collected by the whole class. Use the graphing facilities to produce a bar chart. What is the most common, and the least common, fibre?

Fibre	Property	Fabrics
Cellulose fibres	Cellulose fibres have been used for centuries. They get their name from their chemical structure, which is cellulose, a carbohydrate similar to starch. **Cotton** and **linen** are the most popular cellulose yarns.	denim, canvas, velvet, corduroy, towelling and cotton are all made from cellulose fibres. Other cellulose fibres used to make yarn include hemp, jute, nettle, sisal, ramie and pineapple.
Protein fibres	Protein fibres are produced by animals. They are usually composed of the protein **keratin**. Silk and **wool** are the most common protein yarns.	silk (cultivated and wild), wool, twills, jerseys, felts and velvets.
Regenerated fibres	Regenerated fibres were the first made fibres. They are similar to cellulose fibres as they are produced by breaking down the cellulose in wood to produce cellulose triacetate. **Viscose rayon** was used as a substitute for silk.	encel, viscose and rayon.
Synthetic fibres	Synthetic fibres come from coal or oil. They are made by creating polymer chains. There are hundreds of types of synthetic fibres.	acrylic, modacrylic, polyamide, polyester, elastane, spandex, Lycra, Gor-Tex and PVC.

Activity 7

Create a database showing the names of natural, regenerated and synthetic fibres.

Create a database showing the names and uses of natural (both cellulose and protein fibres), regenerated and synthetic fibres.

Create a database to help select natural (both cellulose and protein fibres), regenerated and synthetic fibres to suit particular textile products. Your database will need to show the names, properties and uses of the fibres.

Group activity: Work in groups to combine your data for entry into a class database. Try to produce a database that could help you select fibres based on their characteristics.

New technology and fibres

If you examine fibres under a powerful microscope you can look at their structure. The structure of the fibre gives it its properties. Some of the newest fabrics incorporate what are called **microfibres**. Technologists discovered microfibres by examining microstructures in nature. Microfibres are thinner than a single strand of your hair.

Technologists can make fibres by manipulating the molecular structure of materials to produce new structures. By using microfibres, designers have made very lightweight fabrics such as Lycra and Gor-Tex. It is possible to make a fabric that is breathable from the inside out (i.e. it lets sweat out) but waterproof (i.e. it keeps rain out). Initially, these new materials were developed for sportswear and people working in extreme weather conditions.

Hybrid fibres and materials

New materials are being invented all the time. Modern industry uses a wide range of what are called **part-textile materials**. Textile fibres are mixed with glass, carbon, metal and ceramics to make high-performance, lightweight materials. These new part-textile materials can be used in many different things, from Formula One racing cars to carbon-impregnated concrete, which has an improved resistance to earthquakes. Ceramic fibres can withstand very high temperatures. This makes them suitable for gaskets and filters.

Activity 8

> Look at the labels of textile products in your home. Collect as many different fibre names as you can. Make a list of the names and say what the fibres are used to make. State which is the most common fibre used in your home.

> Look at the labels of textile products in your home. Collect as many different fibre names as you can. Make a list of the names and the products the fibres are used to make. State which are the most common fibres used in your home. Try to state whether they are natural or manufactured fibres. Highlight which textile products have mixed fibres. Say why you think the designer has used mixed fibres.

> Use the headings **cellulose fibres**, **protein fibres**, **regenerated fibres**, **synthetic fibres** and **mixed fibres** to list the fibres used in a range of textile products in your home. State the fibre properties and say why you think the designers have used them. See how many objects you can find which use new hybrid fibres.

Making Fibres into Yarn

Each type of fibre has its own unique properties. Designers often mix *fibres* together to achieve the best property in the objects they are making. The name given to this is **blending**. The mixing of *yarns* together is called **mixing**.

Activity 9

> Give the names of two fibres that can be mixed with cotton, wool and rayon. State why designers would mix these fibres, describing how they enhance (improve) the properties of the original fibre.

By mixing fibres enhanced properties can be achieved. An example is cotton and polyester mixed to achieve an easy-care yarn which washes and irons more easily. Cotton and wool are mixed to achieve a soft, warm yarn.

How cotton fibres and yarn are made

Nearly half the textiles used in the world are made from cotton. The cotton fibre used to make cotton yarn comes from the cotton plant. To make cotton, the raw fibre, in the form of ripe cotton balls, is harvested. The raw cotton is then broken down using a machine called a **gin**. Cotton seeds have to be removed from the cotton ball before the cotton is ready to make yarn. Each cotton ball contains about 30 seeds.

When the seeds have been removed the cotton fibres can be sorted, drawn into rope and then twisted into yarn. The twisting process is called **spinning**. By altering the amount of twist, the properties of the yarn can be changed. The more tightly the fibres are twisted, the harder and stronger the yarn will be.

The strand of yarn that is produced is called **a ply**. To make a thicker strand, two or more plies can be twisted together. Where four or more plies are put together, the thick yarn produced is then called **a cord**. Cord yarns are not normally used to make sewing thread.

During spinning, the cotton is twisted in a **clockwise** direction to produce an **S twist**, or in an **anti-clockwise** direction to produce a **Z twist**.

clockwise **S** twist   anti-clockwise **Z** twist

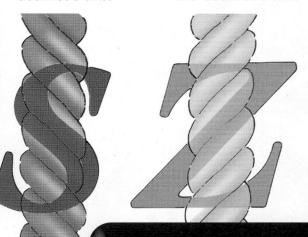

Before the cotton is coloured it has to be **bleached** and **cleaned**.

Texturing yarn

Filament and synthetic yarns are naturally smooth. To produce a range of different appearances, manufacturers use a **texturising process**. Texturising is sometimes done when the yarn is being made. The most common method is to heat the yarn and then to pull it over the edge of a knife.

Today textile designers use a wide range of yarns. Designers have even used metal, rope, telephone cables and garden hosepipe as yarn. Yarn produced from carbon, ceramics and glass is available.

Twisting yarns together

Fine fabrics are made from single yarns. Thicker, stronger fabrics are made from cords (plies twisted together). Often, cords are referred to as **ply yarns**. Whilst they are normally twisted with the spirals running in different directions from the twists in the individual single yarns, special effects can be achieved by varying this rule.

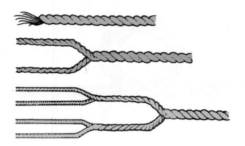

You can twist your yarn into interesting cord for weaving and knitting.

There are straight-twist yarns and there are a number of different twists used to produce textured and fancy yarns. The most common are **slub, nub, bouclé, loop** and **ratine.**

Slub

Slub yarn has an irregular thickness. It is made by adding extra tufts of *fibre* or by loosening the twist. The irregular thickness of the yarn produces a very attractive, uneven finish on the fabric.

Nub

Introducing lumps of *yarn* at regular intervals during weaving produces nub yarn. The extra twists caused by this produce nub yarn's distinctive shape. Sometimes the added yarn is a different colour.

Bouclé

Two yarns are twisted together, but one of the yarns is kept slack. This gives the yarn its distinctive appearance and feel.

Loop

A thick and a thin yarn are twisted together with the thicker yarn being fed more quickly into the machine. This causes it to loop as the thinner yarn is twisted around it. Sometimes the loops are brushed to produce a **mohair** effect.

Ratine

An outer yarn is wound around a core yarn. This outer yarn is looped to create a distinctive texture.

Activity 10

> Make up a poem entitled '**Yarn**' using 12 textile-related words from this section of the book.

> Make up a poem that describes the different types of yarn described in this section of the book.

> Read the text in this section describing different types of yarn and fibres. Using what you have learnt, make up a poem that describes the different types of yarn and fibres and what they look like.

Activity 11

> You can twist your own yarn by hand or by spinning a heavy weight. Make some of your own yarns and plies.

> You can twist your own yarn by hand or by spinning a heavy weight. Make some of your own yarns and plies. Try to achieve interesting effects by varying the lengths of the fibres or yarns.

> You can twist your own yarn by hand or by spinning a heavy weight. Make some of your own yarns and plies. Try to achieve interesting effects by varying the lengths of the fibres or yarns and adding extra fibres or other objects to the twists. Can you reproduce the yarns illustrated in the book?

Making Fabrics from Yarn

To turn yarn into fabric a **structure** has to be produced. There are three main types of fabric: **woven**, **knitted** and **non-woven**. In this section of the book, we will explore these three types, and the methods used to make them.

Activity 12

> Read the following section on different types of fabric and create your own fabric using one of the methods.

Producing Fabrics by Weaving

Warp and weft

Woven fabrics are made by weaving yarns together. The two yarns are woven together using a **loom**. In weaving, the yarns that go from top to bottom of the loom are called **warp** yarns. The yarns that go from left to right are called **weft** yarns. The area in which the weft thread turns is called the **selvage**.

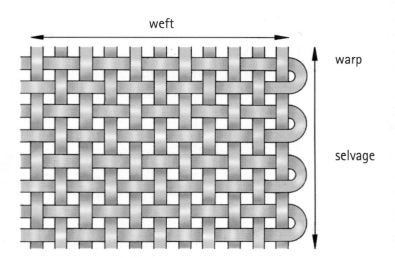

The grain of the fabric

The warp and weft create the grain in fabric. It is important that you can identify the grain. This is because fabric is usually cut with the grain. Sewing patterns have arrows that have to be lined up with the grain of the fabric. Cutting diagonally across the grain is called **cutting on the bias**.

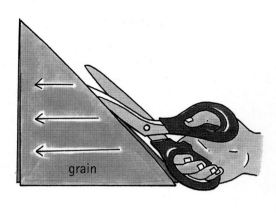

grain

Cutting on the bias

Cutting on the bias changes the property of the piece of fabric. The fabric becomes more flexible and stretchy. Bias fabric can also be curved more easily. Bias binding became popular in England in the 1880s and is still used today. It is produced from fabric cut on the bias.

Activity 13

Think about the criss-cross structure of fabric that is cut on the bias. Why do you think fabric cut on the bias curves more easily?

Activity 14

Find a piece of scrap fabric and pull a single yarn (thread) to find the grain of the fabric. Test the stretchiness of the fabric, both along and across the grain.

Changing the properties of fabric by using different yarn

By changing the way yarns interlace, and how tightly they are pulled together, the structure of the fabric can be changed. Different fabric properties can be achieved. Most of the fabrics you can buy are soft and flexible. The spaces between the threads allow movement. If these spaces were tightened up, the fabric would stiffen. You can make fabric more flexible in one direction than another by closing up the space between either the warp threads or the weft threads. You can also change the way a fabric stretches by using Lycra or other stretchy yarns in one direction.

Changing the colour of fabric

Changes in colour can be achieved by **vertical interlocking**. This occurs when different-coloured weft threads are used. They are linked during the weaving process.

Changing the weave of the fabric

Any type of yarn can be woven with wire. Using wire it is possible to change the stiffness and characteristics of the fabric. You can also add beads to the weave.

Making your own fabric

You can weave fabric yourself using a card or wooden loom.
Any frame can be used to make a loom – even a car roof rack can be used. All types of weaving are variations upon a simple theme.

Use the ridges in corrugated cardboard to help you sort beads and small round objects.

Activity 15

Read the section on types of weave and study the diagrams below. Then create your own fabric.

1 A piece of card or wood is cut into a square or rectangle.
2 Slits are cut at the top and bottom of the card to take the warp threads that run from top to bottom.
3 Wind the warp threads onto the card.
4 Using a needle, weave the weft threads first from right to left, then back under and over the warp threads. Do not pull the yarn too tight, as this would cause the fabric to lose shape when you remove it from the card.
5 Push the threads together using the blunt edge of the needle. The tighter the threads are pressed together, the firmer the fabric. You may want to experiment with different pressures to achieve different effects.
6 Remember you can weave any yarn including wire to add stiffness to your fabric. You can also add beads to the weft part way across. This gives decoration to the fabric.
7 Once you have removed your fabric from the card, thread any loose strands or loops onto a needle and push them back into the fabric. The loose ends can also be tied in groups to create fringing. This will prevent fraying.

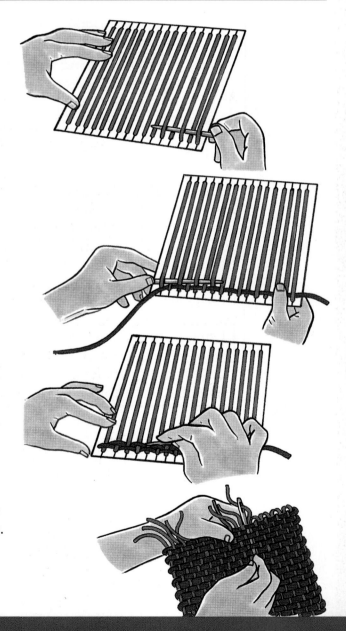

Enhancing the properties of fabric

Chemicals can be used to enhance the properties of fabric and yarn. Fire-retardant chemicals are often used. Starched or resin-coated yarn can add stiffness to the fabric.

Sometimes designers add bone, wood and sticks to the weave to add stiffness to the fabric.

You can join two pieces of fabric together to make two layers. This is called **laminating**. The two layers can be stitched or glued. The layers do not have to be the same – fabric wadding and stiffer fabric can be used, for example.

> Any added decoration must have similar washing characteristics to the product.

You can achieve interesting effects by weaving different fabrics or ribbons together. Once woven, the finished material can be glued or stitched to make it permanent, or laminated to another piece of fabric.

Cut strips of fabric or paper.

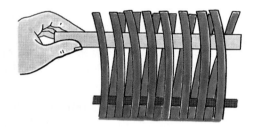

Lay out the warp.

Activity 16

Describe three instances when you think that a special finish would need to be added to enhance the property of the fabric or yarn.

Using textile products used in the home to illustrate your descriptions, describe three instances when you think that a special finish would need to be added to enhance the property of the fabric or yarn.

Using textile products to illustrate your descriptions, describe three instances when you think that a special finish would need to be added to enhance the property of the fabric or yarn. Investigate ways of applying fabric finishes and state how you think the finish could have been applied to each product you chose.

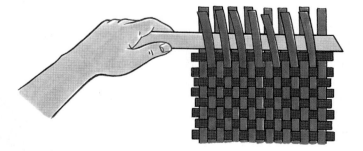

Weave in the weft fixing with glue or stitches.

Types of Weave

The properties of fabric can be changed by altering the structure of the weave. There are many different types of weave, but the most common are:

- plain
- twill
- satin
- hopsack
- rib
- jacquard.

> Care of mixed yarn fabric has to suit the most delicate yarn.

Designers often use different types of yarn in the warp and weft. Microfibres were created by textile professionals after studying microstructures in nature. They are created by actually changing the molecular structure of materials. The name given to this technology is **fibre engineering.** When microfibres were first introduced, both warp and weft used yarn made with them. Today most modern fashion fabrics use microfibres in one direction, usually the weft, to save money.

Activity 17

> Create a piece of fabric using woven strips of fabric. Design and make a bookmark using your new fabric.

> Design and make a bookmark or picture using your own woven fabric. You must not use glue or stitching.

> Design and make a book cover, desk tidy or wallet using your own woven fabrics. Include three-dimensional effects and consider methods of shaping, joining and forming your product without the use of stitches or glue.

Plain weave

Plain weave is the simplest weave, as the weft thread goes over one warp thread and under the next. Plain-weave fabrics are usually very strong and durable. Linen, chintz and gingham are examples of plain weave fabrics. Plain-weave fabrics are used for blouses, shirts and dresses.

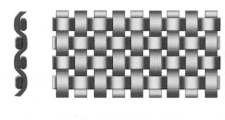

Twill weave

Twill weave is used to increase **bulk** and therefore warmth. Twill weaves are strong. Denim, cotton drill and flannelette are examples of twill-weave fabrics. Twill fabrics are used for denim jeans, sports jackets, uniforms, skirts and trousers.

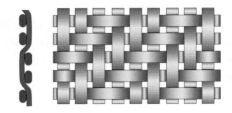 

Satin weave

Satin-weave fabrics are less durable than plain or twill-weave fabrics, but the long, floating threads can catch the light, giving a shiny and lustrous appearance. Silk and rayon are examples of satin-weave fabrics. Satin-weave fabrics are used for scarves, shirts and blouses.

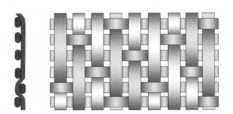 

Hopsack weave

Hopsack weave is sometimes referred to as **basket weave**. It produces softer fabrics than plain weave.

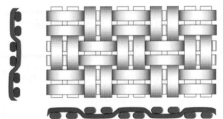 

Rib weave

Rib weave is a variation on plain weave. Fine and coarse yarns are usually alternated to produce a ribbed effect.

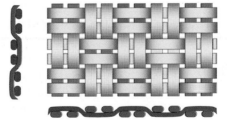 

Jacquard weave

Unlike the straight-line patterns produced in the other weaves, very complicated woven patterns can be created using a jacquard loom. The loom is named after its inventor. Initially, punch cards were used to control hundreds of needles which each lifted individual warp yarns. Today, Jacquard looms are computer controlled. Flowers, animals, patterns and curves can all be created during the weaving process.

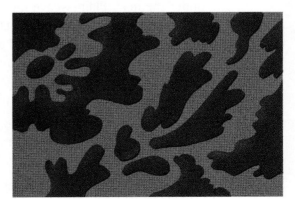

Computers and weaving

Textile manufacturers use traditional and computer technology. Computerised looms allow manufacturers to create complex layered structures that could not have been produced manually.

New fabric structures

In a constant search for new fabrics, scientists and designers have developed new types of woven structures. Inspiration for these new structures has often come from traditional craft. The weave shown here is called **soumak** or **weft wrapping**. It was traditionally used to make rugs.

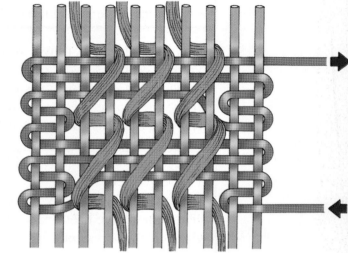

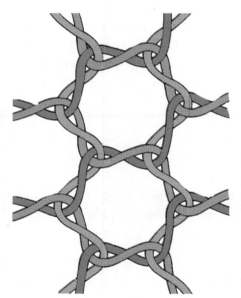

NASA scientists working on **triaxial interlocking weaves** (an example is shown here), to produce very strong lightweight fabrics, developed their own loom called the **Barber–Coleman power loom**. Strong, lightweight fabrics are essential for space travel. Astronauts are subjected to very hostile conditions, with severe temperature changes, and potential pressure loss. Humans would not survive in these conditions without protective clothing.

Crafts people in Ecuador, Africa, Afghanistan, India, China, Japan and the Middle East have been producing very complicated weaves by hand for centuries. Some of these weaves can only be made by hand.

Look at the samples provided by your teacher. Use a magnifying glass to identify the types of weave. Try to collect a number of different fabric samples that have been woven using different types of weave. Stick them into your book and state what weave they have been made with.

Look at the samples provided by your teacher. Use a magnifying glass to identify the types of weave. Try to collect a number of different fabric samples that have been woven using different types of weave. Stick them into your book and state what weave they have been made with. State where designers might use each weave and why you think it would be suitable.

Look at the samples provided by your teacher. Use a magnifying glass to identify the types of weave. Try to collect a number of different fabric samples that have been woven using different types of weave. Stick them into your book and state what weave they have been made with. State where designers might use each weave and why you think it would be suitable. Look at **basket weaving**, fencing and other uses of woven non-fabric materials. Compare the weaving technique used with those used in textile products.

Producing Fabrics by Knitting

Knitting is a traditional craft that dates back to the ancient Egyptians' times. Today some of the world's top fashion designers use knitted fabrics to design exciting and fashionable textile products. Knitting is the second most important way of creating the structures that turn yarn into fabrics.

A wide variety of interesting textile products can be achieved using knitting. It is said that the huge range of sweater knitting patterns comes from the fact that each fishing village would have had its own particular stitch. This enabled villagers to identify shipwrecked fishermen when they were washed up on the shore, alive or dead. During the Victorian era American settlers taught their children, both boys and girls, how to knit.

Forming loops of yarn with needles and pulling new loops through the previous ones creates the structure of knitted fabrics. Knitted fabrics are usually comfortable and crease-resistant. Knitted fabric is also usually stretchy. You can design your own knitting by adding different coloured yarn, using different stitches, adding beads and modifying existing patterns. First let us examine how knitted fabric is made.

There are two basic ways of knitting fabrics, **weft knitting** and **warp knitting**.

The hairier the yarn, the less see-through the fabric.

Weft knitting

Weft knitting uses continuous loops of interlocking yarn across the width of the fabric. It is called weft knitting because the yarns go from left to right like the weft in woven fabrics. Hand knitting uses this method.

There are three main basic stitches in weft knitting, **plain**, **rib** and **purl**.

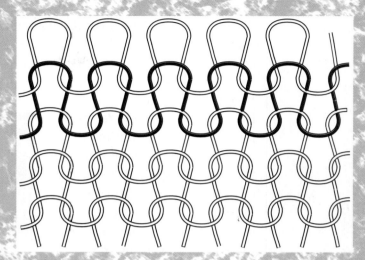

Designs on graph paper are difficult to knit as the length of stitches in knitting is not the same as the width.

Warp knitting

Warp knitting is so named because the yarns run vertically like the warp yarns in weaving. The vertical yarns are locked together by looping on alternate sides. Warp knitting cannot be produced by hand. Warp knitting is used to make very fine lightweight fabrics.

As with woven fabrics the properties of knitted fabric can be changed by:
- altering the space between stitches
- altering the yarn
- chemical treatment of the fabric or yarn.

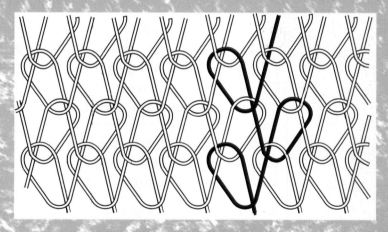

Never machine sew knitting unless you have to. It doesn't stretch enough.

Making your own knitted fabrics

The first thing you need to do to make knitted fabric is to create the first row of stitches. There are two forms of hand knitting: **finger knitting** and knitting with **needles**.

Finger knitting

Finger knitting is easy. You simply produce a loop by knotting the yarn. Then pull the yarn through the loops using your fingers. You can use any thickness of yarn. Rope or natural twine can be used to make a hammock in less than 30 minutes using this technique.

You simply loop rows of finger knitting together to add width.

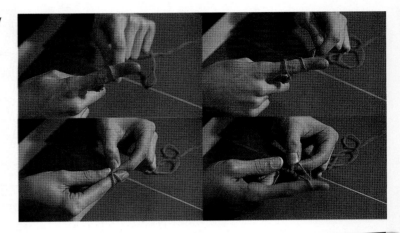

Very fluffy yarns are unsuitable for young children. They can chew them and breathe in the fluff.

Using knitting needles

Two needles are required. In the diagram they have been labelled **L** for left and **R** for right to help explain how to knit. You may want to make labels for your needles to help you follow the instructions.

You should hold the knitting needle as you would a pencil or pen. Hold the yarn around your little finger.

It's the stitch size, not the needle size, that counts.

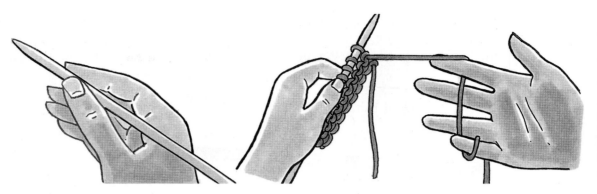

Making a slip knot is the first stage for almost everything you do in knitting.

1 Wind the yarn around two fingers to make a loop, leaving about 15 cm of yarn to pull back through the loop.
2 Pull the thread back through the loop and slide the knot down the yarn. You can use one of the knitting needles to help you if you wish.
3 Put the knotted loop onto the **left** needle.

You have made your first knitting stitch.

If you don't want to put labels on your knitting needles, use two different colours.

Once you have mastered this skill you are ready to start knitting. To start with you will need to produce the correct number of stitches for the width of your knitted fabric. The name given to this is **casting on**. There are lots of ways to cast on, but we will use one of the simplest methods.

Now hold the needle (labelled L) in your right hand and the wool in your left hand.
1 Wind the yarn around your thumb from front to back. Insert the needle under the yarn as shown in the diagram by the arrow.
2 Lift the yarn using the needle.
3 Remove your thumb whilst pulling the long end of the yarn.

Keep repeating this process until you have enough stitches.

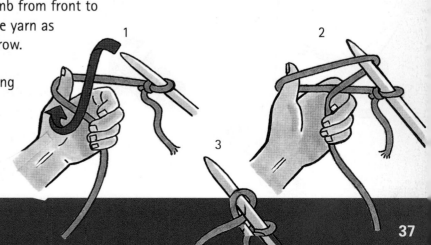

Once you have casted on enough stitches to give you the right width, you are ready to give your knitted fabric length. This is achieved by using knitted stitches. There are a number of different stitches that can be used. We are going to use one of the easiest stitches to learn.

Store knitted fabric folded flat to prevent stretching.

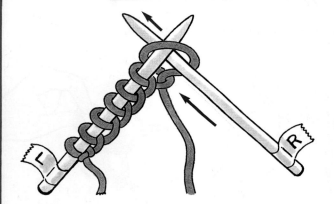

When you have finished casting on, swap the L needle back to your left hand. Hold the R needle in your right hand. Now place the right-hand needle through the first loop from front to back.

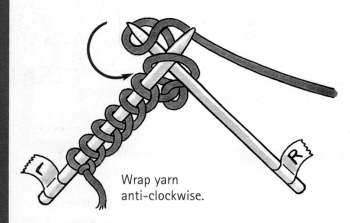

Wrap yarn anti-clockwise.

Wrap the yarn anti-clockwise around the R needle as shown by the arrow and then take it behind the R needle.

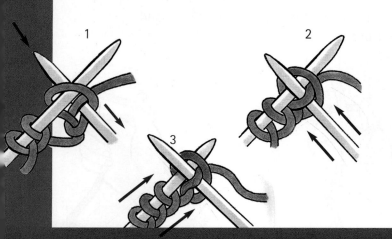

1 Pull the R needle down until its tip touches the L needle.
2 Be careful not to pull it too far or you will lose your stitch. This is called dropping a stitch. It can add useful design effects but causes parts of the fabric to unravel.
3 Now use your left-hand index finger to slide the stitch off the L needle onto the R.

Repeat the process until you finish a row of stitches. Then switch hands and repeat back along the row.

The last thing you need to learn to complete your piece of knitted fabric is how to finish the last row of stitches so that your fabric will not come undone. The name given to this is **casting off**.

Begin with all of the stitches on the L needle. Knit the first two stitches on the row. Then insert the tip of the L needle through the first stitch on the R needle. Now lift the first stitch over the second stitch as shown in the diagram.

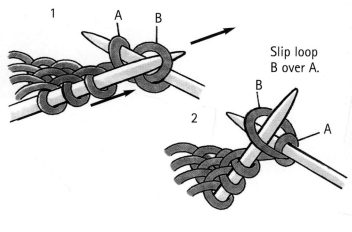

You can now drop the stitch off the left-hand needle leaving the other stitch in the R needle.

You have now learnt how to cast off. Keep going along the row until you are left with one last stitch.

Cut the yarn a few centimetres from the knitted fabric and pull the end of the yarn through the loop of the last stitch. This makes a knot and will stop the knitting from unravelling.

Stitches that change the shape of the fabric

There are a number of different stitches used in knitting. Some give a different texture to the fabric produced. You can also change the shape of the knitting by adding stitches, called **increasing**, and by removing stitches, called **decreasing**. There are a number of ways of doing this, but the two most common methods are called **simple increase** and **simple decrease**.

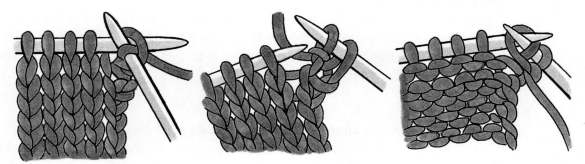

simple increase

  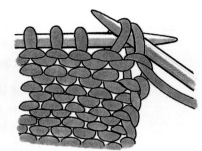

simple decrease

You can also weave fabric and yarns into your knitting, to create different effects.

Activity 19

Use books, magazines and expert advice to find out the difference between a plain stitch, a rib and a purl stitch.

Use books, magazines, and expert advice to explore the different types of knitting stitches and basic stitch patterns. Use notes, cut out pictures and sketches to describe the differences between plain and purl stitches. Using cut-outs, sketches and notes describe the differences between garter and rib patterns.

Use books, magazines and expert advice to explore the different types of knitting stitches and basic stitch patterns such as garter, stocking and rib patterns. Use notes and sketches to describe the differences between different stitches and stitch patterns.

Machine knitting

Knitting machines use a large number of needles in a row. The part of the machine that holds the needles is called a **bed**. These needles produce the knitted fabric. Some knitting machines have more than one row of needles. Knitting machines look very complicated, but they work on a simple basis. Each needle represents a stitch.

Activity 20

Manufacturers use knitted fabrics for a range of fashion items, including sports clothing. Lycra (elastane) is often used to retain the shape of a garment. Explore a range of manufactured knitted fabrics and list the properties you think they have.

Each needle has three important parts:

- butt
- hinged latch
- hook.

Another important part of the machine is the carriage. This slides backwards and forwards over the machine bed and controls the movement of the needles. On most domestic machines, it is moved by hand, but on professional machines, it is motorised. As the carriage moves across the bed, the needles are pushed forwards and backwards.

First, as with all knitting, you need to cast on. Casting on creates the first series of loops. On the knitting machine, as each needle moves forward, it picks up a piece of yarn and pulls this through the last loop to produce the next loop.

Look carefully at the diagrams to see how this works. First the hook pushes through the loop, with the latch pointing backwards 1. The hook picks up the yarn, and as the needle comes back again, the loop turns the latch over onto the hook 2. The latch then opens up the loop and allows it to slip off the needle as the yarn is pulled through 3, leaving the next loop on the needle 4.

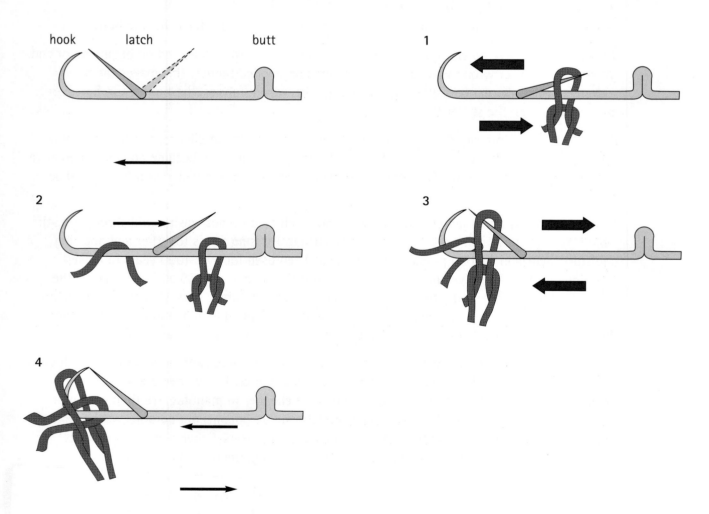

Activity 21

Design and make a simple knitted headband or armband.

Design and make a knitted piece of jewellery suitable for an 11-year-old. You should think about colour and decoration.

Use knitting to design and make a piece of jewellery suitable for an 8-year-old child. Your jewellery should reflect a cultural theme.

Bonded Fabrics

Bonded fabrics are made by holding fibres together through bonding. This can be achieved in a number of ways. The commonest of ways are:

- Gluing fibres together with resin adhesive
- Stitching fibres together with thread
- Heating fibres and compressing them
- Pushing a needle through massed fibres to encourage them to intertwine and bond.

Bonded fabrics have no warp or weft, no grain, no right or wrong side, and no beginning or end. There is no right or wrong way to cut out patterns on bonded fabrics. This makes them extremely versatile and cost effective to use. As with woven fabrics, the tighter the fibres are pressed together, the stiffer the material.

Tradition and folklore say that bonded fabrics were invented when pilgrims packed their new sandals with sheep's wool to prevent blisters. The fibres of the wool became bonded together to make a fabric. In the Middle East there is a similar story about a traveller who filled his shoe with camel hair.

If you put your woollen jumper into the washing machine on a hot wash it will shrink to a stiff board. You will have made a bonded fabric called **felt**. Pressing fibres together and applying moisture, heat and friction produces felt. Felt has been used for over 1000 years to make clothing and tent-like dwellings. Felt was used in Turkey in about 6500 BC. This makes it the oldest method of making textile products. Today it is used to make hats, slippers, blankets, toys and jackets. It is pliable and versatile. Felt can be used in appliqué and embroidery. Bonded fabrics can be shaped during manufacture. Felt hats are shaped as they are made.

You can make your own bonded fabrics by pressing together fibres and bonding them with glue. Traditionally, natural fibres were used to make bonded fabrics. Today, they are also made of regenerated and synthetic fibres. Bonded fabrics are cheaper to manufacture than woven or knitted fabrics. Modern bonded fabrics like Tyvek (made by DuPont) are durable, washable and chemical-resistant. They do not fray and can be cut using lasers. Other non-woven fabrics include J-cloths, tea bags and Vilene, used for interfacing garments, and mending.

You can make your own bonded fabrics by pressing fibres together.

Activity 22

> Using felt, design and make a simple picture for use as a teaching aid with a child of 4 years.

> Felt can be used to make simple games for young children. Design and make a simple game based on farm animals for a child of 4 years.

> Felt can be used to make simple finger puppets. Design and make a finger puppet based on a cartoon character.

Foams and rubbers

Foams are now used extensively in the production of textile products. They are created from synthetic polymers. They blend well with other fabrics and can be cut and carved like clay.

Glass

Fabrics made from glass fibre are growing in popularity as they are not affected by sunlight, mould or moths. Fibre optics are made from glass. They are used in the telecommunications industry. A number of textile manufacturers are investing in this new technology.

Choosing the Right Fabric for the Job

When you choose a fabric you need to consider a wide range of properties including stiffness, weight, weave, texture, colour, price and width. The list below shows a few of the properties you may wish to consider.

Property	Ask yourself
Abrasive resistance	Does the material wear well? Does it go bobbly after a few washes, or snag and fray?
Appearance	How does the fabric look and feel?
Absorbency	Does the fabric absorb moisture?
Colourfastness	Does the fabric's colour run when wet, or does it fade in the light?
Crease resistance	Does the fabric crease easily?
Colourability	Does the fabric accept fabric dyes?
Cost	How expensive is the fabric compared to others with similar properties?
Drape	How does the fabric hang?
Durability	Is the fabric hard-wearing?
Flammability	How does the fabric react when burnt?
Elasticity	Does the fabric recover its shape when stretched?
Pest resistance	Is the material resistant to moths?

Property	Ask yourself	*continued*
Strength	Is the fabric strong?	
Texture	Does the fabric feel good to the touch?	
Thermal properties	Is the material a thermal insulator or conductor?	
Warmth	How good is the fabric at keeping in heat?	
Waterproof	Is the material waterproof or shower proof?	
Washability	How easily does the fabric wash? Does the fabric shrink when wet?	

The chart below indicates the properties of some common fibres used in the production of fabric. The more stars shown, the more the fibre has the property. For example, for cost, 1 star is less expensive than 5, and for durability, 1 star is less durable than 5.

	Durability	Strength	Flammability	Warmth	Elasticity	Absorbency	Colourability	Cost
Cotton	★★★★	★★★★	★	★★★	★★★★	★★★★★	★★★★	★★
Silk	★★★★★	★★★★	★★★	★★★	★★★★	★★★★★	★★★★★	★★★★★
Wool	★★	★	★★★	★★★★★	★★★★★	★★★★★	★★★	★★★★
Nylon	★★★★★	★★★★★	★★★★		★★★★★		★	★
Polyester	★★★★★	★★★★★	★★★★	★			★	★
Rayon	★	★★★	★			★★★	★	★
Lycra	★★★★★	★★★	★	★	★★★★★			★★
Glass fibre	★★★★★	★★★★★	★★★★★					★★★

You can use the chart to help you choose the right fibres for a particular product. For example, a tea towel would need to be absorbent, durable and relatively low-cost. Cotton has these properties.

Activity 23

> Using the chart, what fibres would you choose to make a warm jumper, a tablecloth and a hand towel? Describe the properties of the material you have selected.

> Select three fibres from the chart and describe their properties. Give two examples of textile products made from your chosen fibres. What properties do you believe to be important in the design of these textile products?

> Select three textile products that are used in the kitchen. Now look at the chart and select two fibres that could be used in the manufacture of your chosen products. Describe the properties that you feel are relevant to your chosen products, explaining both the benefits and drawbacks for each fibre.

Fabric finishes

We have seen the fabric properties related to the characteristics of the fibres, yarn and manufacturing methods; and finishes can be added to fabric after weaving and knitting. Some fabric finishes are decorative and others are functional. We will explore decorative finishes in the next section of the book. Now we are going to look at functional finishes.

Functional finishes

Functional finishes improve the properties of fabric. Removable tags are often placed on textile products to show you what finishes have been applied. Finishes can change the way fabric takes colour and dyes. They can change the feel, wear and performance of the fabric. The chart below describes some of the common finishes.

Finish	Property
Anti-bacterial	Anti-bacterial finishes help to make the fabric resistant to perspiration and body odours.
Anti-static	Anti-static finishes reduce the build-up of static electricity on manufactured fibres.
Bleaching	Most fabric is bleached to remove unwanted colours and to soften the fabric.
Carbonising	Softens the texture and helps the fabric to take dyes by removing grease and oils in the fibres.
Crease resistance	Special chemicals are added to prevent creases.
Flame proofing	Chemicals are used to make the fabric resistant to flames. Another word used to describe this is **flame retardant**.
Glazing	Adds a polished or glazed surface to the fabric, making it more resistant to dirt.
Mildew proofing	In some countries humidity levels are high. This causes some fibres, particularly cellulose, to go mouldy. Chemicals are added to the fabric to stop mould and mildew from forming.
Moth proofing	Chemicals are added to deter moths and other insects.
Napping	Increases the warmth and softness of the fabric by brushing the surface of the fabric.
Shrinking	Weaving stretches the fibres; manufacturers often shrink them back to stabilise them so that they will not shrink in the wash.
Stain resistance	Chemicals are added to prevent staining.
Stiffening	Chemicals are added to stiffen the fabric, making it firmer or even permanently pressed.
Waterproofing	Fabrics can have wax or resin applied to make them waterproof or water repellent. Some fabrics are naturally water repellent because of the fibres and weave of the fabric.

Applied (or added) finishes enhance the property of the fabric but can also cause problems when you want to clean the textile product. Many of these finishes wash out if the product is not cleaned correctly.

Activity 24

Textile products can be improved by applying fabric finishes. Describe one different finish you would apply to each of the following textile products:
- a child's nightdress
- a carpet
- a tent
- a chair cover.

State why would you apply these finishes.

Select five textile products used in the home. Choose at least one item of furniture, at least one textile product for use outside and at least one item of clothing. Appropriate finishes are often used to enhance textile products. State which of the finishes described in this textbook could be used on your chosen textile products and why.

Appropriate finishes are often used to enhance textile products. Look at the list of property-enhancing finishes described in this textbook. Describe one textile product that would benefit from each finish. For each textile product say why the finish would be appropriate.

Testing Fabrics

There are a number of tests that you can carry out on fibres and fabrics to find out about their properties. Remember to ensure that each sample is of a comparable size. This is necessary to give a fair test.

Durability
Stretch your fabric around a wooden block. Rub with a pumice stone or sand block for a given length of time. How well does the fabric wear? Think about how you could measure this.

Strength
Add more and more weights to stretch a thin section of the fabric or fibre until it breaks.

Warmth
Place a thermometer or electronic temperature censor in a test tube. Fill the test tube with water heated to a set temperature. Hold the thermometer in place with a bung. Wrap the test tube in a piece of fabric. Use a fabric sample of the same size for each test. Record the temperature every five minutes. Compare the results from different fabrics.

Elasticity

Stretch a piece of fabric of a set size with weights over a set amount of time. Use the same weight for each test. Remove the weights and measure the size of the sample. How well does the fabric return to its original size?

Absorbency

Weigh the piece of fabric. Soak with water and weigh it again. Time how long the fabric takes to dry.

Colourability

Try to dye a sample of each fabric.

Flammability

Burn a small piece of the fabric and note the effects of the flame, colour of flame, smell and smoke. How quickly did the fabric or fibre catch fire?

 This type of test must be carried out under strict supervision as some fumes are hazardous.

There is also the obvious danger of the fire spreading.

Technologists often use flammability tests to find out which type of fibre is in a sample. Special booths are used to prevent dangerous fumes from escaping and to prevent the spread of fire.

Fibre	How it burns
Cotton	rapidly with a yellow flame, leaving a soft grey ash
Silk	slowly, sizzling and curling away from flame, leaving black ash
Nylon	slowly and shrinks from the flame, melting into a hard, grey bead
Polyester	slowly, melting and giving off a black smoke, leaving a hard black bead

Other tests could include:
- washability
- crease resistance
- stain resistance
- waterproofing.

Activity 25

Chose three of the tests outlined above and compare a range of knitted, woven and bonded fabric. Check with your teacher if you want to do a flammability test. Write down the results of your test.

Design and carry out a test to see how woven, knitted and bonded fabric made from a range of fibres and finishes responds to washing. Experiment with a range of fabrics and note down the results of your test. Think about shrinkage and colourfastness.

Design and carry out a test for washability: look at stretch, shrinkage, colourfastness and creasing. You must test woven, knitted and bonded fabric made from a range of natural and manufactured fibres and with a range of finishes. Try to predict how different fabrics will respond to your tests. Build a database to show how a range of fabrics respond to your tests and how accurate your predictions were.

Sewing

Hand sewing

A wide range of needles is available for hand sewing (see pages 12–13). There are a number of stitches you can use when hand sewing:

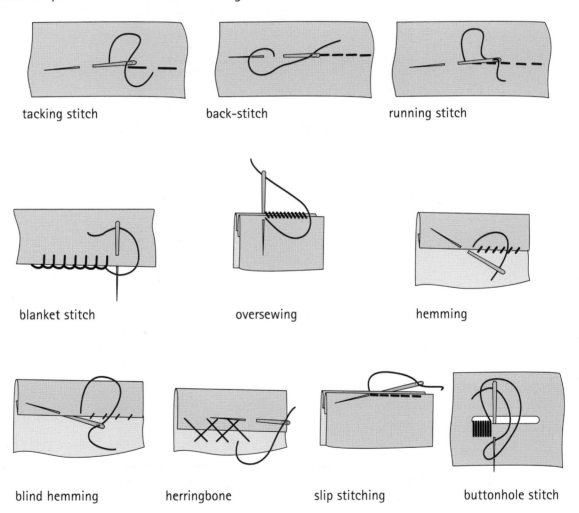

tacking stitch   back-stitch   running stitch

blanket stitch   oversewing   hemming

blind hemming   herringbone   slip stitching   buttonhole stitch

Machine sewing

Sewing machines use two threads. One of the threads is kept in a **bobbin** held inside the machine; the other comes from a reel at the top of the machine. The needle uses both threads and forms interlocking loops. It is essential to make sure that the **tension** (tightness) of both threads is correct. Using the sewing machine controls it is also possible to change the size of the stitches.

Embroidery

Embroidery is a traditional technique used for decorating fabrics. Thousands of different effects can be created using different threads and stitches. Embroidery threads are stitched into the fabric to form a pattern. Interesting line, shape, texture and colour effects can be achieved. Braids, lace and ribbons can be used for embroidery.

There are two methods of embroidery: traditional **hand embroidery**, and **machine embroidery**. For hand embroidery it is usual to place the fabric on an embroidery ring before embroidery. This holds the fabric and prevents it from being pulled out of shape.

Hand embroidery

Hand embroidery is one of the most effective ways of decorating textiles. Very intricate designs can be added to fabrics by hand embroidery. Hundreds of different types of thread can be used, including wool and metallic threads. There are large numbers of special stitches used in embroidery. The most common include **brick**, **chain** and **cross** stitch. Embroidery can even be used to achieve a three-dimensional effect. Using thick threads and overstitching raises the height of the stitch.

You can renew an old garment with embroidery, stitching and decoration.

Brick stitch

This stitch is called brick stitch because the pattern looks like bricks. It can be vertical as shown in the illustration, or horizontal. If you work the same stitch twice it is called **double brick stitch**. Three times is **triple brick stitch**.

Each brick is the same size.

If you vary the size of the bricks to produce alternate long and short stitches you produce what is called Parisian stitch.

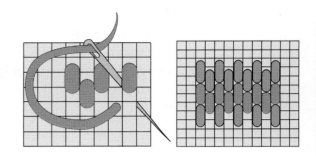

Chain stitch

Chain stitch gets its name because the pattern looks like chains. You can use chain stitch to make fabric look like knitting.

To do chain stitch you need to loop the thread under the next stitch.

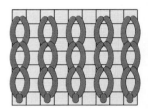

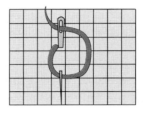

Cross stitch

Cross stitching is very popular as it is versatile and attractive. Some embroidered garments are entirely produced using cross stitch. The stitch itself can be produced either as in the illustration, by making half of the cross in one direction first, then working back to produce the second part of the cross, or by making each cross individually. Other similar stitches are **goblin**, **half cross** and **smyrna**.

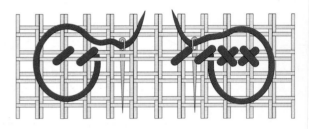

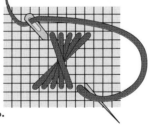

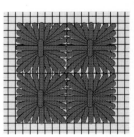

Rhodes stitch

Rhodes stitch creates interesting raised squares. To do the stitch follow the diagram carefully. Add the small central stitch last to hold the crossed threads in place.

Leaf stitch

Leaf stitch is used to reflect the shape and patterns of leaves. Leaf stitch is often worked in different colours to add shade and tone effects.

Activity 26

Produce a sample of each of the stitches shown above.

Machine embroidery

Most modern sewing machines are pre-programmed to produce embroidery stitches. When you first look at a modern sewing machine, you are faced with a range of knobs and patterns. It is best to experiment to find the preset stitches you like best. You may need some help.

Sewing machines have a number of special feet made for embroidery. Machine embroidery threads have to be very strong. Machine embroidery threads are soft and have fewer twists so that they lie flatter on the fabric. There are a large number of special embroidery threads available including metallic threads. The tension setting is very important for embroidery. If your embroidery distorts or puckers, you can try loosening the tension and shortening the stitch length.

The secret of machine embroidery is to combine different stitches to achieve new patterns.

Some machines can be linked to a computer. You can design a logo or embroidery pattern on the computer screen, and the pattern is transferred onto the fabric. In industry, computer-controlled machines are used to produce badges, logos, patterns and motifs, by embroidery.

It is normal practice to add an iron-on interfacing to the back of the fabric before embroidery. This helps to prevent the fabric stretching as it passes under the machine foot.

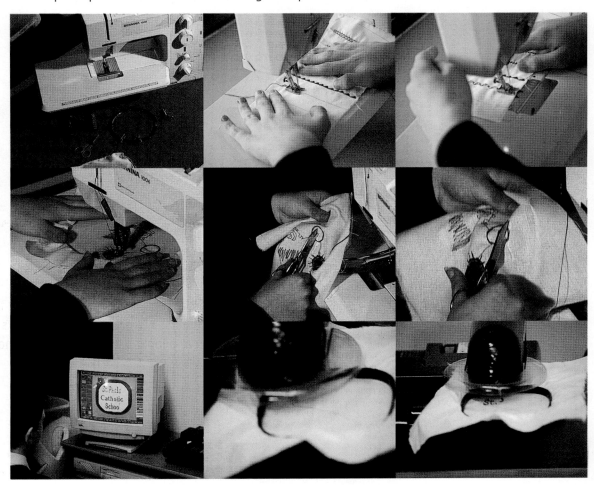

Activity 27

Use a sewing machine and simple stitches to create patterns. Your teacher will show you the type of patterns and stitches you could use.

Use a sewing machine to create free machine embroidery patterns based on a selected picture. The picture could be a postcard or a photograph of your pet, for example.

Use a sewing machine to create free machine embroidery patterns based on a selected picture. The picture could be a postcard or a photograph of your pet. Think about colour, shape and size.

Designing Textile Products

The design brief

Before a designer can start to design a textile product he or she has to work out what the customer wants. The best way to explore this process is to follow through a simple design and technology activity. Let's explore the design of an oven glove. The first stage is to establish the **design brief**. The design brief tells us exactly what we are going to design. It contains a short statement of intent. To write a design brief we have to ask a number of questions, such as:

- Who will use the product?
- Why would they use it?
- Where would they use it?
- When would they use it?
- How would it be used?

In our case the designer has been asked to design an oven glove for use in a local restaurant. The design brief is: *to design an attractive and imaginative oven glove to protect the hand of the user from burns when removing hot pans from the oven.*

The first stage of the design process is to analyse exactly what is needed. Asking our list of questions will help us to define what is required. Adults will use the glove, so it will be designed to suit an adult hand. They will use it to remove hot pots and pans, so it will have to protect them from the heat. They will use it in the kitchen, so it must be hygienic. It will be used all day, so it needs to be durable.

The next stage is to look at similar gloves and to look at how they are made and used. We could use surveys or questionnaires with potential customers. We could interview cooks or parents. We could look in books or catalogues. We could observe people using oven gloves and search the Internet. It is important to write down the findings of this research.

The design specification

Once we have conducted the research, we can create a **design specification**. The design specification is a list showing what the glove must be able to do. The design specification will contain some fixed things and some things that can be changed through the design process. The design specification should contain at least 10 to 20 statements including things like materials, usage, size, cost and methods of manufacture.

A Design Specification for an Oven Glove
- The glove must be safe.
- It must insulate the user from heat.
- It must not be coated in poisonous fabric finishes or anything that will burn.
- The glove must be hard-wearing.
- The seams must be strong so that the glove does not split in use.
- It must be the right price.
- The glove must be the right shape and size for an adult.
- The glove must be washable to be hygienic.
- It must be easy to find the glove in a busy restaurant kitchen – it could be brightly coloured.
- The glove must be flexible to enable the user to grip pots and pans firmly.

Design review

When you have designed and made your textile product you can use your design specification to see if your finished design is suitable. The design specification shown above could be used to evaluate the finished oven glove.

Activity 28

Use the specification checklist to help you to draw up a specification for the oven glove described above. Part of the chart has been completed for you.

Specification	Reason
1 Flame proof	To protect the user from burns.
2 Washable	For hygiene reasons to avoid food contamination.

You could devise your own tests to ensure that the fabric which is selected for the glove is suited to the product specification.

Activity 29

In a previous activity you wrote a design specification for an oven glove. Now get an oven glove and test it against your specification. Does it meet the requirements?

In the previous activity you wrote a design specification for an oven glove. Draw up a list of tests you could carry out to see if the glove meets the specification. Now get an oven glove and test it against your specification. Does it meet the requirements? What other properties does it have?

In a previous activity you wrote a design specification for an oven glove. Draw up a list of tests you could carry out to see if the glove meets the specification. Now get an oven glove and test it against your specification. State the benefits and drawbacks of the glove and to what degree it meets the requirements of your specification. What other properties does it have? What fabrics have been used, and what properties do they have that help the product meet the specification?

Designing a Decoration for Your Textiles

The name given to the drawings of logos and designs that are placed on textile products is **cartoons**. These are not the same as the cartoons shown in magazines and on the TV. The word refers to the actual design of a flower, leaf or logo to be incorporated in the textile product. When you design your cartoon for a textile product you must think about the structure of the fabric.

Designs for textiles can be drawn on graph paper to help transfer them onto the fabric structure. You can also use grids to enlarge or reduce your designs.

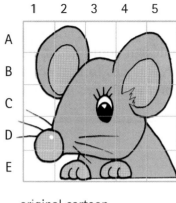

original cartoon

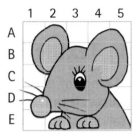

reduced cartoon

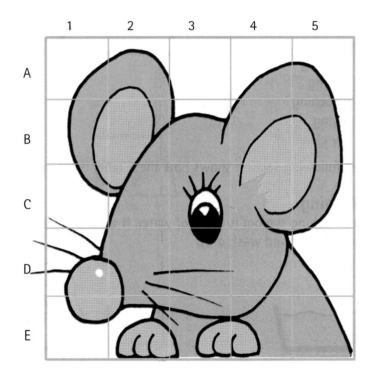

enlarged cartoon

Activity 30

Using graph paper design a simple leaf cartoon (or something similar) that could be embroidered onto a textile product.

Dry cleaning

A simple circle is used to indicate dry cleaning requirements. A number of modern textile products can only be dry cleaned. Dry cleaning uses chemicals to remove dirt and stains. Some new fabrics even require specific cleaning chemicals. A letter inside the circle indicates the chemicals that can be used.

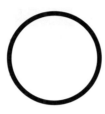

all solvents
may be used

perchlorethylene
only

special fluoro-carbon
solvent to be used

Drying

A square indicates drying requirements. Symbols inside the square show you how the textile product should be dried. Some fabrics lose their shape if they are not dried correctly.

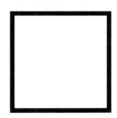

dry flat

drip dry

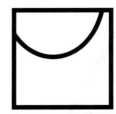
line dry (hang)

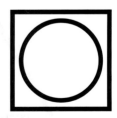
tumble dry

Do Not ...

If a cross is placed through the symbol it means do not treat in that way. For example:

DO NOT iron

DO NOT wash

Remember that some fabrics will fade if they are dried in direct sunlight.

Activity 31

Copy the washing instructions from the labels of five textile products found in your home. Say what each label means.

Find five textile products in the home that have care labels. At least one product should be dry cleaned only. Copy each label and produce a simplified drawing of the product. Annotate your drawings to say what each label means. For each textile product explain the main properties of the fabric and why you believe the care instructions say what they do.

Find five textile products in the home that have care labels. At least one product should be dry cleaned only, and one product should be non-iron. Copy each label and produce a simplified drawing of each product and its label. Describe the differences in the care instructions. Explain the main properties of the fabrics and say why you believe the care instructions are what they are.

Test

1. What are the three ways of making fabric by joining fibres together?
2. Where do natural fibres come from?
3. What is a filament fibre?
4. What is a hybrid fibre?
5. Draw a slub yarn and a loop yarn. How are they made?
6. What is the difference between warp and weft?
7. What does 'cutting on the bias' mean?
8. Draw plain, rib and satin weaves, annotating your drawings to show the difference.
9. What is the difference between warp and weft knitting? Use illustrations.
10. Describe five properties of fabric that you need to consider when designing a textile product.
11. Describe seven fabric finishes, illustrating your answer by referencing appropriate fabric finishes to specific textile products.
12. Describe three fabric tests.
13. What is a design brief; what is a design specification?
14. What is a care label and what information is usually shown on it?

Section 3

The Fashion Industry

Designing Textile Products

As we have seen, when designing textile products, it is important to consider the **function** and look of the finished product. Function means the job the product does for the user. In the previous section of the book you explored the properties of fabrics. In this section you will learn about design, fashion and **culture**. Design is concerned with colour, pattern, texture and shape. We will also look at shape in more detail in the next section of the book..

Getting ideas

You can find ideas for your textile designs from a range of sources. History, geography and art books feature tapestries, people in national or historical costumes and natural forms. Children's story books often feature mythical creatures, simplified drawings and letter forms. Biology books contain flowers, birds, fish and animals. Physics books feature structures and microscopic textures.

Leaflets and magazines also contain pictures and illustrations that can give you ideas for textile designs. Look for pictures of nature, buildings, bridges, maps and patterns.

Activity 32

Choose a theme, for example natural or industrial, and create a theme board using pictures you have collected.

Choose a theme, for example natural or industrial, and create a theme board using pictures you have collected. Now collect a range of pictures from magazines and catalogues of fashion items and add them to your theme board. How do you think the designers were influenced by your theme?

You are going to produce a theme board illustrating the way fashion designers draw on nature and the made world for inspiration. Collect a range of pictures from magazines and catalogues of fashion items and other pictures and add them to your theme board. Explain the links you find between the fashion items and other pictures.

Colour

Every day we are bombarded by colours. Colours can affect how you feel. Some make you feel happy, others, sad.

Colour plays an important part in fashion and design. It is important that you understand how to mix colours to produce other colours.

The correct name for the range of colours is **hues**. The human eye can recognise three properties in colour. These are hue, **value** and **intensity**. The word colour is a general term used to describe the effect of hue, value and intensity. We will examine each of these aspects of colour.

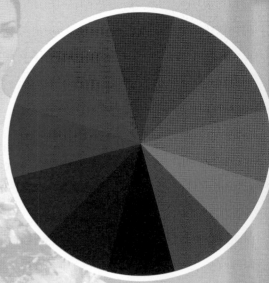

Primary colours

All colours are made up from three basic hues: **red, yellow** and **blue**. The name given to these hues is the **primary colours**. Mixing two adjacent hues produces the colours on this colour wheel. A colour wheel is a vital aid to textile designers.

Hues

Hue is the name given to a colour to distinguish it from another. For example, red is a different hue from blue.

Secondary colours

There are three **secondary colours: orange, green** and **purple**. These are made by mixing together any two of the primary colours. Red mixed with yellow makes orange; yellow mixed with blue makes green; blue mixed with red makes purple.

Tertiary colours

Tertiary colours are created by mixing a primary colour with a secondary colour.

Value

Each colour can also be mixed with black or white. The lightness or darkness of a colour is what gives it a value. Adding white to a colour creates what is called a **tint**. Adding black to a colour makes what is called a **shade**.

Intensity

As well as being a different hue (colour) and value (light and dark), colour can be bright or dull. This is called its **intensity**. A hue can be bright and of high intensity or dull and of low intensity. Usually the closer a colour is to a primary colour, the more intense or bright it will be.

Using colour in your textile products

To design great products, you need to understand how to design using colour. To do this you need to understand how colours **mix**, and colour relationships.

Colour relationships

All colours need light for us to see them. Colours also react with each other. Look at the coloured squares below. They are all drawn in equal proportions, yet they appear to be different sizes. This is due to the effects of the colour relationships. This means the way the colours react with each other. In this example the colour relationships create an **optical illusion**.

Activity 33

Collect a range of pictures where colour is important, for example where it is used to create a mood or to attract you, or for camouflage. Your pictures can be taken from sources such as the natural world, building interiors or the fashion industry.

Colour relationship is very important in fashion design as one colour can significantly affect the way we see another. Look at the four circles below. The inner circle is the same colour in each case, but the surrounding colour significantly changes the way we see the inner circle.

Activity 34

Draw a range of shapes and fill them in using different colours to change the visual effect. Computer graphics programs offer an ideal way of exploring colour combinations.

Draw a range of shapes and fill them in using different colours to change the visual effect. Describe the different effects. Computer graphics programs offer an ideal way of exploring colour combinations. Now write a poem about colour, matching moods to the likes and dislikes of your family.

Collect a number of pictures showing the way colour is used in the fashion industry. Now draw a range of shapes and fill them in using different colours to change the visual effect. Describe the different effects and how they are used in the fashion industry. Now write a poem about the effects of colour and shape in the fashion industry.

When designers talk about colour relationships they use two terms: **harmony** and **discord**. When a colour is in harmony with another, the effect is pleasant and comfortable. When it is in discord, there is a visual imbalance. The colours seem to fight with each other, emphasising their difference. Other names for these two effects are **complementary** and **contrasting**. Harmonious colours complement each other. Colours in discord contrast with each other. Using this knowledge you can create interesting visual effects.

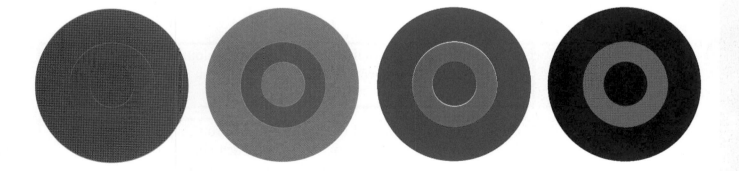

Harmonious and contrasting colours

There are two ways of achieving harmonious colours. One way is to use similar colours together. The other way is to use complementary colours. Colours on the opposite side of the colour wheel (see page 61) are always complementary to each other. Colours which appear striking together are said to be contrasting. To achieve contrasting colours, use colours which stand out and fight with each other, or use black and white as they both intensify other colours.

Activity 35

Which of the following colours would you say are hot colours, and why? Blue, red, green, purple, yellow, white, black. Make a list of all the colours you can think of, starting with the hottest colours at the top of the list and finishing with the coldest at the bottom. This will give you your own colour temperature rainbow, which you could use to help you in your textile designs. Discuss your rainbow with other members of your class. How does it differ from theirs?

Colour influences the way we feel. Designers often describe colours in terms of their relationship to each other and in terms of the way they make the viewer feel. Words like warm, vibrant, dominant and aggressive are used. The colour red speeds up the body's metabolism. Red is seen as being striking, passionate, warm, demanding attention and young. Pink is associated with romance; deep red is aristocratic. Yellow on a good day makes us lively and happy – it makes us think of sunshine and flowers. But if yellow is too bright, we tire of it very quickly and it can also make us irritated or distracted. Green, on the other hand, is restful; blue is often cool or cold; purple is sophisticated and brown is natural and rustic. Black is often linked with evil and death.

Activity 36

Look at the cultural differences in attitudes to colour. Different cultures use colour in different ways. Explore the use of colour for specific occasions, such as weddings, funerals and festivals. Present your information in an interesting way, showing any cultural differences you have discovered.

When choosing colours, you need to consider the effects you want to achieve. Try using words like striking, tranquil, exciting, natural, warm, cold, young, feminine, surprising and masculine when you draw up your design specification.

Activity 37

Choose three colours you think go well together. Draw the colours on a piece of paper and say why you think they work well together. Can you say how the colours make you feel?

Choose three colours you think go well together and three you think do not go well together. Draw the colours on a piece of paper and for each colour state what emotion you think it generates. Say why you think the colours do or don't work well together. For each colour state what textile product it could be used on.

Choose three colours from nature. Draw the colours on a piece of paper and for each colour state what emotion you think it generates. Say why you think the colours do or don't work well together. Now choose three bright colours. For each colour say what emotion you believe it generates. Remember to use emotive words like fierce, passionate and young. For each colour selected state what textile product it could be used on and why you think it could be suitable for your chosen product.

Activity 38

Using only the three primary colours, design a simple decoration for a child's pocket.

Colouring Fabrics

Fabrics can be coloured in a variety of ways. The fabric can be coloured at any stage of manufacture, from dyeing the fibres, the yarn or the whole garment once it has been produced. Fabrics can be dyed a single colour. Some of the most attractive, multi-coloured designs are produced using special techniques like **batik** and **tie-dye**. Both of these techniques are covered later in the book (see pages 88 and 84). Before you can dye fabric you need to understand what dyes are and what they will and will not do.

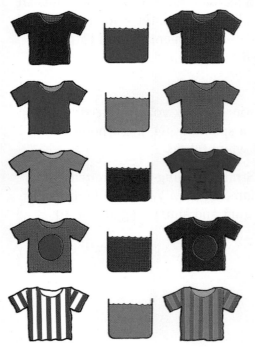

Dyes

Dyes are colours made from chemicals or plants. Dyes are all around us.

Dyes do not build up on the surface of an object like paint; they are **absorbed** into the fibres of the fabric. This means that, if the fibres are already coloured, the new colour will blend with it, not cover it. You can use your knowledge of colour theory to predict the end result.

For a fibre to accept a dye it must absorb it. Before you dye fabric it must be clean and free from anything that will stop the fibres absorbing the dye. Stains and dirt will not be covered by dye – they will show through. Faded areas of fabric will take more colour than non-faded areas. Folded or creased areas of the fabric will absorb less dye than flat, ironed fabric. Fabrics made with natural fibres tend to dye more easily than manufactured fabrics because they are absorbent.

Long before the synthetic powder-based dyes we use today were available, people used plants to dye fabrics. Dyes made from plants are called **natural dyes**.

Always remember that, if you are dyeing coloured fabric, you will be combining colours. If you dye yellow fabric with blue dye the result will be green.

Natural dyes

Berries, flowers, leaves and bark can all be simmered with water to make dye. Dyes produced from plants, rocks and animals are called natural dyes. Early dyes consisted of **minerals** ground into **pigments** and mixed with tree resin, wax or blood. Sometimes they were mixed with egg white to produce a paste that could be painted direct onto the fabric. A large number of plants produced natural dyes – blackberry shoots produce black dye, red cabbages produce red dye, seaweed makes brown dye, onion skins and heather give gold and yellow, and spinach produces olive green.

Natural dyes often produce different colours on protein fibres and cellulose fibres. Some natural dyes will work only on protein or cellulose fibres.

Dye	Colour on protein fibre	Colour on cellulose fibre
Coffee beans	Brown or grey	Cream
Sunflower petals	Yellow	Bright pink or creamy yellow
Heather flower tops	Warm yellow or fawn	None
Dried tea leaves	None	Browns, fawn and grey

One of the problems with natural dyes is that they wash out easily. In technical language, they are not **colourfast**. To make the colours more colourfast, a **mordant** must be used. Mordants are important in natural dyeing. Mordants are used commercially to help **fix** the colour. Protein and cellulose fibres often need different mordants. Salt can be used as a mordant with cotton and linen (cellulose fibres). Vinegar is a mordant with wool and silk (protein fibres).

Activity 39

You are going to use fruit and vegetables to dye fabric. For this you will need: fruit and vegetables, a saucepan and lid, a sieve, a wooden spoon, a jug, a teaspoon, a small amount of cream of tartar and some pieces of white fabric.

Boil the fruit or vegetable in water for 30 minutes. Strain, keeping the coloured liquid. Bring the liquid to the boil, add the mordant and simmer gently. Wash the fabric and rinse well. Then add a piece of damp fabric to the liquid and simmer again for 30 minutes. Remove the fabric, rinse and dry.

 Wear gloves and an apron.

Synthetic dyes

Synthetic dyes produce brighter and more intense colours than natural dyes. They are also cheaper to produce. Different fibres react differently to synthetic dyes. Synthetic dyes are made from chemicals. It is important to get the right synthetic dye for the material to be coloured. A mordant is also used to make the fabric colourfast when synthetic dyes are used.

Fabric Textures

Textile products have both colour and texture. The texture can be examined by touch and sight. The name given to the way a fabric looks is **visual texture** and to the way it feels is **tactile texture**. All fabric has a texture, due to the fibres it has been made from and the way it has been made. The feel of the fabric when we touch it is very important. Fabrics which are nice to touch and handle are more attractive to us. Some fabrics can feel very different even though they are made from the same fibres. Harris tweed and lamb's wool are both made from wool. Tweed is rough and knitted; lamb's wool is very soft. Other fabrics have a very distinctive feel: satin is shiny, nylon is slippery and velvet is smooth.

Fashion designers often experiment with different visual and tactile textures. They do this by changing or mixing fibres, by changing the way the fabric or product is made and by adding to or modifying the fabric after it has been made. For example, if the visual texture of a fabric is changed, it can be made to look like lace, plastic or metal. If the tactile texture is changed, it can be made to feel like paper, rubber or velvet.

We use a range of words to describe a texture:
- broken
- solid
- wavy
- rough
- bumpy
- soft
- smooth
- rough
- undulating (wavy)
- coarse.

Activity 40

Produce a collage of fabric pieces to illustrate texture.

In its natural state, a knitted fabric made from natural fibres will normally have a rough texture. A satin weave fabric made from filament fibres will have a smooth texture. Visual textures can be applied to finished fabric by printing. By altering the physical or surface properties of the fabric, a range of visual and tactile effects can be achieved.

For more on textures see pages 25–26.

Activity 41

Collect 10 scraps of different fabrics, each about 12 cm². Now try to change the texture of the fabric using your own ideas or some of the ways listed below:
- use pinking shears to give a serrated edge
- pull some of the weft threads
- remove some of the weft threads
- brush with a coarse comb, wire brush or teasel to fluff up the surface
- push holes through the fabric
- fold the fabric
- screw it up into a ball or wind it around a pencil very tightly.

Describe, using notes and drawings, the different effects you achieve with your samples.

Some industrial methods use chemicals to distort the surface of fabric. Other methods include the use of glues, rubber, foil, varnishes and binders to achieve puff effects, gloss effects and **puckering**.

You can achieve interesting texture effects by **distorting**, **dévoré** or **adding** to the fabric. These techniques are discussed later in this section.

Activity 42

> You can record examples of textures by a technique called rubbing. Simply place a sheet of paper over a textured surface and rub with a crayon or coloured pencil. Use rubbing techniques to collect a range of textures. You should collect at least five textures. Try to describe the textures you find using emotive words.

> Designers use textures from nature to influence their ideas for new textile finishes. You can collect textures by a technique called rubbing. Simply place a sheet of paper over a textured surface and rub with a crayon or coloured pencil. Using rubbing techniques, collect a range of natural textures that could be used on textile products. You should collect at least 10 different textures. Choose five of your textures and state why you believe they would be suitable for a textile product.

> Textile products can have both a natural texture, due to the way the fabric has been made, and an applied texture. Designers use textures from nature to influence their ideas for new textile finishes. You can collect textures by a technique called rubbing. Think about applied textures and how they can be achieved. Use rubbing or drawing techniques to collect a range of textures that could be used on textile products. You should collect at least 15 different textures. Choose five of your textures and state why you believe they would be suitable for a textile product. Say how you think they could be achieved.

Distorting

Manufactured fibres can be affected by heat. Designers use this to create interesting three-dimensional textures.

Puckering is achieved by distorting the surface of the fabric with resin or chemicals, which causes the fibres to shrink. This shrinking affects the tension in the weave of the fabric, making it crinkle.

 The chemicals used are very dangerous as they are based upon caustic solutions. **Caustic solutions burn the skin.**

The chemicals can be applied directly or by using **resist** techniques. The fabric is first stretched and the caustic solution applied by printing or brush. The caustic solution physically alters the fibres wherever it is applied. The solution also changes the colour of the fabric where it is applied. All sorts of effects can be achieved, ranging from **embossed** areas to **crimping**.

Whilst these techniques are not possible in school, you can distort fabric to create texture using glues and stitches.

Dévoré

The word dévoré comes from the French *dévorer*, to devour. The dévoré method uses acid or chemicals to dissolve away areas of fabric. The result is similar to lace. Resist techniques can be used to protect the areas that the designer does not want removed. Alternatively, the fabric is

produced with two yarns, one of which will be affected by the acid, the other not. It is very important to ensure that the warp and weft are made from different yarns, or the fabric can fall apart.

The most popular industrial technique uses a chemical which, when heated, releases an acid that burns away cellulose fibres but does not affect protein fibres. The chemicals often affect the colour of the fabric as well as the texture.

You can achieve a similar effect to dévoré, using special **dissolving fabrics**. The example shown is an embroidery on cold water-soluble fabric. The fabric looks a little like cling film, and is sold under a variety of names. If you embroider a design on the water-soluble fabric and then dissolve the fabric, you are left with the stitches. It is important to ensure that you create a geometric grid to hold your design in place when the fabric is dissolved.

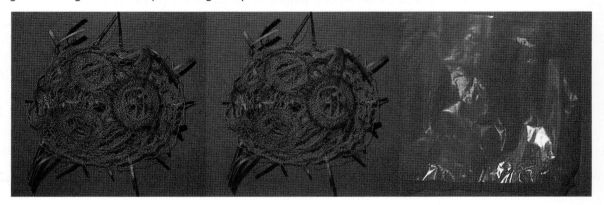

Adding
Adding rubber or an expanding pigment to a fabric can be used to achieve puckering and distorting. There are a number of **puff pigments** available on the market. Most are applied on the back of the fabric and then heated using an iron or hairdryer. They work best on stretchy fabrics such as Lycra and organzas.

To use one of these puff pigments, you must first stretch the fabric. Apply the binder to the back of the fabric using a brush or by printing. Be careful not to apply too much paste as it will pucker the fabric too much. Allow to dry. Remove the fabric from the stretcher and heat with an iron or hairdryer.

There is a wide range of rubber solutions available on the market, but these are harder to use than puff pigments and cannot be coloured using fabric dyes. Rubber solutions produce similar effects to the puff pigments described above.

By using industrial processes, a wide range of special effects can be achieved, including **flocking** and **plastic coating**. Flocking is dangerous because the fibres float in the air and can cause serious breathing problems. It is usually achieved by adding glue to the fabric and then adding fine flocking fibres to the glue. A magnetic field is used to keep the flocking fibres on end whilst the glue sets. Flocked fabrics do not wash well as the flocking fibres come off during the wash.

Transparent fabrics

Lightweight transparent fabrics are often used to create three-dimensional effects.

Pattern

Patterns can be printed or drawn onto fabric. Ideas and influences can be taken from nature or from the made world, such as architecture. Some patterns are traditional. We will explore these in more detail later in the book. For now we will explore natural forms and how these can influence fabric design and fashion.

Once you become aware of the shape and texture of the natural things around you, you will begin to see how they can act as an inspiration for your textile product designs, just as they do for professional designers.

Wood, flowers, fruit and vegetables are valuable references for exploring pattern and natural colours. Pattern in nature changes all of the time, because things are always growing.

Activity 43

Keep a scrapbook of feathers, pressed flowers and leaves, and drawings of stones and trees or cut-outs from magazines showing butterflies, birds, fish and animals.

Drawing around leaves, feathers and shells can produce interesting outlines that can be incorporated into your textile designs. Some shapes, like spiders' webs, are intricate and detailed. They can be put onto textile products using stitching and printing techniques. Other shapes are bold and highly textured. They can be made into three-dimensional or two-dimensional designs by using other techniques.

Mathematics and textiles

Mathematics plays an important part in textile product design. Measuring and calculating quantities and costs is very important. Lines and geometric shapes are often used in creative design. Stripes and squares are common, as are polygons and curves. Space and proportion also play an important part. Look at the stars below. One is not in proportion. This is because there is a large amount of blank space. Normally designers try to use the space to create a feeling of proportion. Of course, designers sometimes use this effect on purpose to *create* the feeling of space and to draw your attention to the shape.

Focal points

Designers also change the position of the shape to achieve a different feeling and effect.

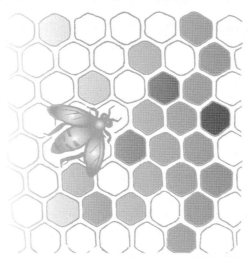 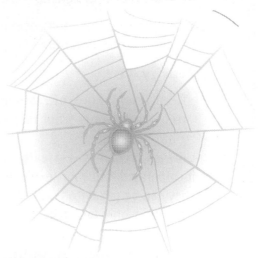

Activity 44

Cut out a small geometric shape such as a star. Change its position in a square border. Where do you think it looks best?

If you use graph paper to produce your textile designs, you can easily alter the proportion by enlarging or reducing your designs. The graph paper also reflects the grain in the fabric.

Stripes

When any surface is divided into larger and smaller sections by vertical, diagonal or horizontal lines, stripes are produced. There are thousands of stripes all around us, from the unique fingerprints from our fingers to the stripes produced by the skyscrapers in our cities. All of these stripes are valuable sources of inspiration for fashion designers.

By varying the widths and spaces between the lines, interesting patterns can be achieved.

When using stripes, try to balance the spaces between the lines. Don't make the spaces the same width as the lines. You can make the lines symmetrical or asymmetrical.

Stripes are used in a large number of textile products, from furniture to garments.

Activity 45

Make a list of all of the textile products you can think of that incorporate striped fabrics. Find samples of striped fabric and make a mood board by stitching them onto a sheet.

Stripes can be found in nature too. These patterns can be used to inspire new designs. Look at the stripes formed by the trees in the picture.

Activity 46

Draw the striped pattern of your thumbprint. You could use a magnifying glass.

Designers can simplify designs from nature. These designs can be on textile products, presented as textures, patterns and colour. The drawing below shows a simplified onion.

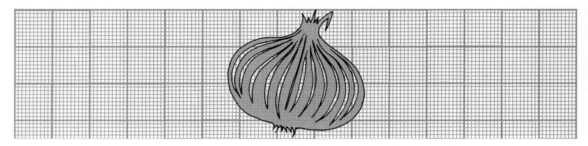

Activity 47

Experiment with different patterns made by drawing straight lines with a ruler, parallel motion board and set square.

Squares

In nature there are no squares, yet we are surrounded by made squares and rectangles. Our buildings, our school textbooks, our doors, windows and bags are all rectangular or square. Woven fabric has a rectangular or square structure, and throughout history designers have used this to good effect. Wherever two lines cross and intersect, a chequered surface is produced. Traditional Scottish tartan and modern fabrics often incorporate a chequered surface.

Don't be afraid to experiment with squares to achieve interesting effects. They do not have to be symmetrical and can be simplified into a stylised design.

Squares can be placed diagonally on the fabric to produce diamond shapes and mixed to produce interesting patterns.

Activity 48

Draw a series of simple geometric patterns to make a simple design. Try to form letter shapes using only geometric patterns incorporating straight lines. Do not use more than three simple geometric shapes.

Activity 49

Textile designs are often taken from nature. Cut an onion in half and draw the stripes created by the layers. Colour in the layers using natural colours to create an interesting design.

Textile designs are often taken from nature. Cut an onion in half and make two drawings to represent the stripes created by the layers. Colour in the layers using natural colours in one of your drawings and contrasting colours in the other.

Textile designs are often taken from nature. Find a range of shapes from nature. Your designs should incorporate squares and stripes. One of your designs should incorporate contrasting colours, one complementary colours and one natural colours.

Borders

Printing or embroidering borders onto fabrics is one of the oldest methods of decorating textile products. Borders are used to **adorn** fashion garments. They are created by putting **ornaments** next to each other. The word ornament comes from a Latin word which means to adorn. Early Egyptian garments were adorned with flowers in rows. In the past, Indian boys from weaving families would lay leaves and flowers in a row to learn the art of designing textile patterns. The leaves would then create an original floral design. The textile designs they produced are renowned throughout the world for their beauty and craftsmanship.

For more on embroidery see pages 49–52.

Activity 50

Pick a number of leaves and lay them next to each other in a row. Think about the best colour for the background and the position of the leaves. Then glue the leaves in place and trace the outlines.

Pick a number of leaves and lay them next to each other in a row to illustrate a theme, for example autumn or spring. Think about the best colour for the background and the position of the leaves. Then glue the leaves in place and trace the outlines.

Pick a number of leaves and lay them next to each other in a row to illustrate the theme of growth. Think about the best colour for the background and the position of the leaves. Then glue the leaves in place and trace the outlines. Describe how your border illustrates the theme.

If the leaves are laid in a curve, they form a **garland**.

You can make borders by using simple geometric shapes. Border patterns usually fall into the categories of plants, animals, geometric shapes, lettering and figures.

Activity 51

Design a border using squares and lines. Add colour to your border.

Design a border using squares, lines and letters. Your border should be decorative and colourful. Think carefully about your choice of colours and thickness of line.

Design a border using squares, lines and letters. Your border should reflect a hot summer's day and appeal to a young child. Think about shape, pattern and colour choice. State why you have chosen the colours and shapes for your border.

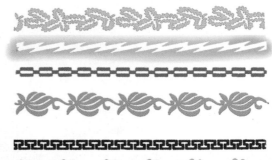

Using pattern

Designers have to be careful when they use pattern as our eyes do not always see the truth. Look at the lines below.

They are perfectly straight and parallel to each other, but we do not see them this way. They create what is called an **optical illusion**.

Similarly the two curved fabric pieces shown below are the same size. The distance between arrow points a and b, and b and c is the same. Measure it if you are unsure.

Designers can use optical illusion to good effect. They can use line and shape to make you look fatter, slimmer, taller, and more shapely.

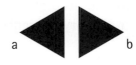

When you select fashion clothing, think carefully about shape, line and form. If you don't it could have a negative effect on your appearance.

Simplifying designs

To simplify means to make simple, less complex and easier. Before you can turn your design into a textile product, you must learn how to simplify it. To do this you will need to learn how to reproduce form, pattern and colours, but within a simplified form. Designers often emphasise decorative techniques and play with colour. Throughout history, images have been created from natural forms. You can produce your designs by hand or by using a computer. The example shown uses both methods.

It uses a favourite picture or postcard. The picture has been simplified to make it possible to reproduce the image on a textile product.

Once you have simplified your design, you can print it onto your fabric as a surface pattern or ornament. We will look at different ways of achieving this in the next section of the book.

Activity 52

You are going to design a surface decoration for a textile product using nature as your source of inspiration. You can use simplification so that your design can be transferred onto a textile product. You should concentrate on looking for ideas which feature line and shape. You should start by collecting a number of different ideas. You can develop the best one later. Use the following words to help you:
- line
- tone
- shape
- colour
- scale
- distortion
- three-dimensional.

Your design will be used to decorate a textile product once you have learnt the techniques and skills necessary to transfer it onto fabric.

Getting Your Designs onto the Fabric

To produce your design on fabric, you will have to draw an outline. The easiest way of transferring your design onto fabric is to use **carbon paper** or any of the special markers and pencils available from textile suppliers.

Air-soluble felt-tip markers
These markers are ideal for transferring your designs to fabric. You can draw on the fabric using the marker. The markers use a temporary ink which fades from view after about 24 hours.

Tailors' and dressmakers' chalk
Dressmakers' chalk is used to transfer designs onto fabric. Traditionally, the chalk was sold as a wedged-shaped white or yellow block. Today you can buy dressmakers' chalk in pencil form. You can brush the chalk off the fabric once the design has been stitched.

Water-soluble felt-tip markers
You can use water-soluble felt-tip markers to draw your design directly on the fabric. Some markers have an eraser built into them. Alternatively, you can use a cotton bud moistened with water to remove the lines. You should always try this type of marker on a spare piece of fabric first.

Adding Colour Effects to Textiles

There are a number of ways to add colour effects to textiles. A large number of dyeing and printing techniques have been developed over the centuries. The main methods are **resist techniques, printing techniques** and **direct application** techniques.

Printing techniques include **block printing, screen printing** and **transfer printing**. Direct application techniques include the use of **fabric paints, fabric pens** and **fabric crayons**. Resist techniques include **tie and dye, tritik, batik** and **silk painting**.

Printing Techniques

Before learning how to print, you need to understand how to repeat your design. The design can be very simple, or extremely complicated and intricate. Printing works by using a **print block** or **stencil** to apply colour to the fabric.

For more information on transferring designs to fabric see pages 54-55.

These networks can be used to give different repeat patterns from the same print block or stencil.

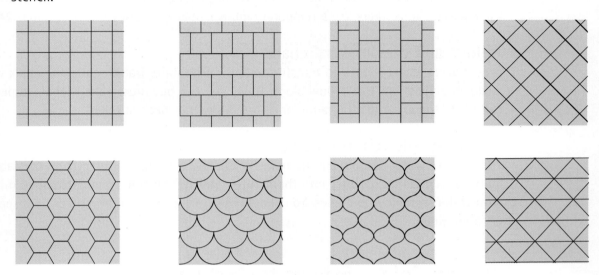

To get more than one colour onto fabric you need more than one stencil or print block. You could use one pattern or stencil and keep cleaning it, but it is easier to have one for each colour. Printing is usually done one colour at a time. Of course, you do not need to print more than three colours, plus black and white, as these colours mix to make all the other colours (see pages 60–62).

Block printing

Block printing is one of the oldest ways of putting designs onto fabric. Egyptians used it in the fifth and sixth centuries. They carved their designs in blocks of wood using knives and chisels. Other materials such as lino, cork, sponges and potatoes can be used to make print blocks.

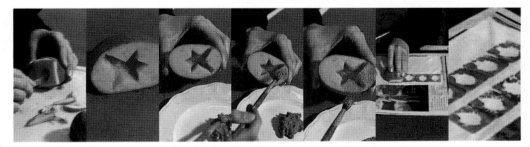

Print blocks can be made by~hand or by using a CNC milling machine.

Block printing works by simply dipping the block into ink and then pressing it onto the fabric, leaving a print.

Relief printing is similar to block printing. You simply paint a waterproof adhesive onto the surface of thick card and stick down a string or thread to create design.

A large number of modern fabrics are printed using a similar principle to block printing. The design is etched onto copper rollers. The rollers pick up the colour from a dye bath and transfer it onto the fabric. The technique is called **roller printing**. This is a good method for printing large quantities of fabric.

Activity 53

Design and produce a sample of block-printed fabric. The theme for your sample should be 'the seasons'.

Using stencils

Stencils are one of the easiest ways to get repeat designs onto fabrics. Usually, you would make a stencil by cutting the negative image out of card or thick paper. Pre-cut stencils are available from craft shops and decorators' stores. The North American colonists were the first to exploit stencilling in the eighteenth century.

By placing the stencil on the surface you want to colour, you mask the surface where you do not want to apply colour.

Stencilling is achieved by using a firm brush or sponge to stipple colour onto the surface. You must ensure that the colour is the right consistency, or it will run under the stencil.

Simplifying a design to produce a stencil is a key step in the process. Your stencil must hold together.

Activity 54

Design and produce a sample of printed fabric based on stencil techniques.
The theme for your sample should be 'flowers' or 'sport'.

Screen printing

Screen printing is similar to stencilling. It is the most versatile printing method. The stencil is put beneath or on top of a meshed fabric. The colour is pressed through the mesh using a device called a squeegee. All areas are printed except those protected by the stencil. It is believed that the Japanese invented screen printing. They would join the small pieces of their stencils together using human hair.

You can use a paper stencil with screen printing, but there are far more sophisticated ways of producing the stencils on the mesh. These methods mean that you do not have to worry about the stencil holding together. Stencils can be painted direct onto the screen or printed photographically onto the screen.

Photographic screens

Very complex designs can be printed using photographic screens. All sorts of flat objects, from photographs to feathers and leaves, can be used to make a stencil. The screen is coated with **photosensitive coating** and allowed to dry. The image is then placed on the screen and the screen is exposed to light. To work effectively the image must not let light through. Where the light hits, the photosensitive coating is fixed. The screen is then washed. The areas of the screen which were shielded from the light wash away. The screen is then used to print as described for screen printing.

Activity 55

Design and produce a headscarf or tie using screen printing techniques. The theme for your product should be 'music'.

Transfer printing

Transfer printing is popular because, unlike block printing and stencilling, it allows all of the colours to be applied at the same time.

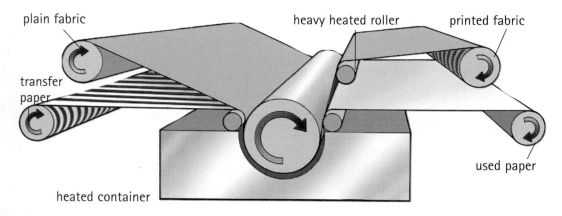

plain fabric

heavy heated roller

printed fabric

transfer paper

used paper

heated container

Transfer printing is used in industry to print large volumes of fabric. The design is printed first onto a roll of paper. Heat and pressure are used to transfer the image from the paper onto the fabric. It is a very fast method of applying the image to fabric.

You can do transfer printing yourself using transfer fabric crayons. See page 84 for instructions. You can also use a computer and special inks to produce a transfer.

Activity 56

Design and produce a wall hanging based on transfer printing techniques. The theme for your sample should be 'my favourite food'.

Direct Application Techniques

The variety of exciting designs that can be produced by direct application techniques is endless. There are a large number of specialist fabric paints, pens and crayons available on the market. Direct application techniques require only a limited amount of equipment.

Paint sticks
Paint sticks consist of oil-based pigments moulded into chubby crayons. They are available in a wide variety of colours. You can also get metallic colours in this form. Metallic colours give an appearance of metals such as gold and silver. You can apply colour to fabric by using the crayons, or by brushing on the colour to achieve interesting effects. You can also place the fabric over textured surfaces before applying the paint sticks. The colour is fixed to the fabric by allowing the paint to dry for 48 hours and then heat sealing it using a hot iron. You must make sure that the iron is not set at too high a temperature for the fabric being used.

Fabric paints
Fabric paints consist of fabric dyes that have been mixed with emulsion to produce a creamy paint. They are available in a wide variety of colours. You can create interesting textures using brushes, sponges and print blocks. There are two types of fabric paint: water-based and steam-fixed.

Water-based fabric paint
Water-based paint is fixed to the fabric using an iron. This heat seals the paint in a similar way to using paint sticks. Water-based paints stay on the surface of the fabric. They are permanent and effective. Water-based paints are ideal for cotton, silk, rayon, viscose and wool.

Steam and fibre-reactive paints

Steam-fixed paints or fibre-reactive paints penetrate the fabric. The colour from these paints is brighter, but the paint has to be fixed by steaming the fabric. Steam-based paints are ideal for silk, wool and nylon.

Silk paints

Silk paints are much thinner than fabric paints. They cannot, therefore, be used for printing. You can, however, achieve interesting effects with a brush or by spattering the paint. Silk paints can be used on most natural fabrics and some synthetic fabrics. There are a large number of silk paints available, including many which are water-soluble. You can add water to water-soluble paints to make the colour paler.

Transfer crayons

Transfer crayons are an excellent way to produce bright, vivid patterns on a very wide variety of fabrics. The technique is called **transfer printing**. Colours may be applied one at a time, or all at once. Very interesting effects can be achieved by layering one colour over another. This creates blends and tonal changes. To use transfer crayons, you first produce your design on a sheet of white paper. This produces a **transfer**. You then place your transfer, colour side down, onto the fabric. To transfer the design from the paper to the fabric, you place a cloth over the paper and press with a hot, dry iron. Transfers can be used up to five times. The colour reduces with each use, but this can be used to good effect.

Activity 57

Design and produce a sample of fabric using direct painting techniques. The theme for your sample should be 'insects' or 'motor transport'.

Resist techniques

With resist techniques, part of the fabric is protected from the dye by wax or thread. There are three main types of resist method: **mechanical**, **physical** and **chemical**. The oldest methods are mechanical and physical. They rely on a physical barrier, such as a tight fold, stitch or crease, to prevent the colour from reaching a part of the fabric.

Tie and Dye

For tie-dying, material is folded and tied tightly with thread. Tie and dye is a physical resist method. A physical barrier prevents the dye from reaching all of the fabric. By folding the fabric in different ways, a wide range of effects can be achieved. A soft, blurred effect is the typical characteristic of a tie and dye fabric. This is caused by the dye partially penetrating the part of the fabric that is tied off.

It is a good idea to experiment with this technique, using a small piece of fabric. Different strings and threads and different tightnesses will achieve different effects. Where more than one colour is used, it is important to add the lightest colour first and to remember that the colours will combine. Red and yellow will make orange, for example. When choosing colours, refer to the colour wheel on page 61.

Using clips and pegs for tie-dye

Clips and pegs can be used to hold the fabric whilst dying. Fold the fabric and then hold with bulldog clips or pegs.

Fold the fabric.

Position bulldog clips diagonally on the edge of the fabric.

Use pegs and folds to create patterns.

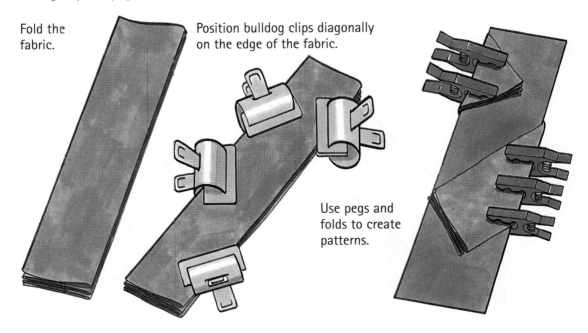

Random tying

Simply draw up the fabric using your fingers and tie with thread. Do this randomly over the fabric.

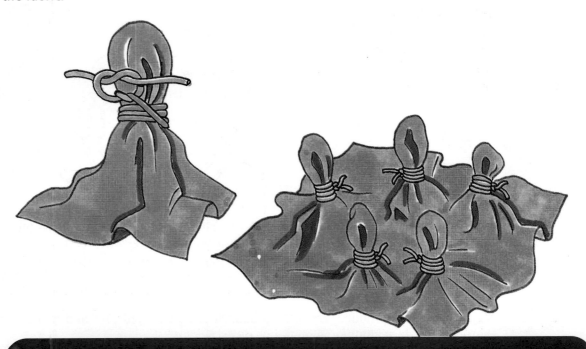

For more on colouring fabric see page 85.

Rolled and tied

Fold the fabric in half diagonally then roll it up. Bind it with thread at regular intervals.

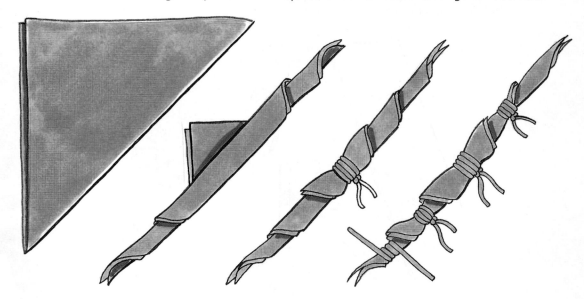

Ruching

Roll the fabric around a folded piece of string. Then gather the fabric up along the string and tie the string ends.

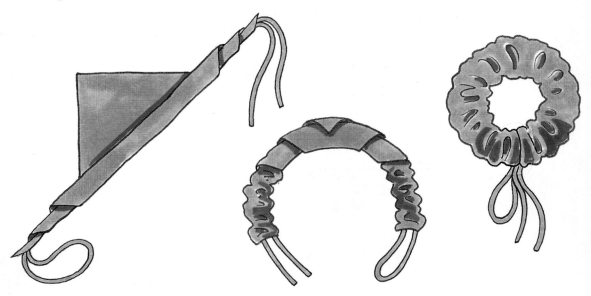

Rubber bands, paper clips, wire and pipe cleaners can be used to tie fabric. All produce different effects. You should consider the type of fabric you are using when choosing the method of tying. Fine cotton and silk need fine thread; looser weaves work better with string and pegs.

You could draw your design on the fabric first, if you want a regular repeated pattern.

Malaysian textile products are often produced using tie-dyed yarn and fabric. The name given to the technique is **mengikat**, meaning to tie.

Stitching (tritik)

Tritik is the name given to a form of dying which uses stitches rather than tied thread to resist the dye. The method comes from Malaysia. Tritik usually results in a more regular and controlled pattern. You can use hand or machine stitching. Simply fold the fabric and then overstitch the design.

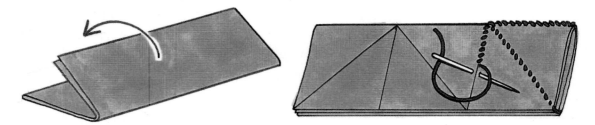

Achieving special effects

A range of different tie and dye effects can be created by tying soya beans into the fabric, using stitches of polyester thread, binding marbles in the fabric, using pegs, clips or plastic strips, or wrapping the fabric around wood, plastic sheeting or metal.

Common effects include:
- **marbling** by crumpling the fabric into a ball and binding the ball of fabric with thread
- **knotting** by rolling the fabric and then tying it in a knot
- **clump tying** using objects like buttons, corks, matchsticks, coins, shells and pebbles
- **stripes**, achieved by pleating or folding the fabric
- **starbursts**, made by pinching the fabric
- **circles**, produced by tying the fabric around round objects. You can lay the objects at random or place them carefully to achieve a regular design.

Reverse tie and dye

In reverse tie and dye the fabric is prepared in the same way, but bleach and colour remover are used on coloured fabric to produce a white pattern.

Activity 58

> Design and make a child's mobile using two of the textile decoration techniques described in the book.

> Design and make a child's mobile based on the theme of 'birds'. Your mobile must incorporate at least three of the textile decoration techniques outlined in the book.

> Contrasting colours, shapes and textures are an important part of mobiles used in cots to amuse tiny children. Design and make a mobile using textiles and a range of techniques to produce interesting effects.

Cultural influences

In some parts of India, tie and dye fabrics are called **bandhani**. The designs and colours are linked to religious customs. The most important bandhani in Gujurat is the gharchola, the wedding sari. In Japan tie and dye is known as **shibori** and in Indonesia as **kembanagan**. In Africa, wealth, class and status were demonstrated by the quality of tie and dye fabrics. The dyeing process was usually carried out by men.

Activity 59

Try to build a picture of any traditional influences that your class and their families have about tie and dye fabrics and fabric decoration. Ask parents and grandparents if they know of any particular design or cultural uses of tie and dye. Share your findings with your class.

Batik

Batik is a very ancient method of colouring fabrics. The name batik comes from Indonesia and means wax writing. Batik is drawing your design with wax. It is a mechanical resist method. Mechanical resists rely upon the creation of the physical barrier between the dye and fabric. Wax is the most common barrier used to prevent the dye from reaching parts of the fabric. Other resists include fat, mud, resin, clay, gum, starch and even soya cheese. Java is famous for its batiks developed over the centuries.

Natural fibres are the best for batik work as they are more absorbent. Synthetic fibres are less absorbent, so they do not take the wax or dye as well.

Batik is used in traditional fabrics from India, Japan, Africa and China, and Egyptian tombs have been discovered containing batik textiles. In the 1920s, batiks were the height of fashion in Britain.

Traditionally, designers use hot wax, although today we can also use cold wax. The hot wax often cracks during the dyeing process, and this gives traditional batik fabrics a characteristic called marbling. In West Africa, paste resist is more common than wax. Cassava paste is applied by hand, scratched, combed or painted onto wooden blocks and then pressed.

Activity 60

Design and produce a sample of fabric using batik. Before you start, it is best to draw your design onto the fabric. The theme for your sample should be 'through the microscope'.

Wax resist

A wide range of wax can be used, including the wax from candles, paraffin wax and beeswax. Traditionally, the wax mixture used for batik is 50 per cent beeswax and 50 per cent paraffin wax. Paraffin wax cracks easily, producing a crackle effect called marbling.

Hot wax can be very dangerous as it behaves like fat in a chip pan. You should always use the correct equipment and have a fire blanket to hand. Traditionally, the wax is melted in a pan within a pan. A container of wax is placed in a large pan containing gently simmering water. Water is used to warm the wax gently and to stop the wax from overheating. Special care is needed to stop any water mixing with the wax as this can cause spitting. This type of water bath is called a **bain-marie** in cooking.

Using special batik pots is the best and safest method to melt the wax. This is what you will use in school if you use hot wax to create your batik.

Activity 61

Find out how the water in the bain-marie stops the wax from overheating. Why must a bain-marie never boil dry?

Applying the wax

The special tool used for applying the wax is called a **tjanting**. They were first used in Java. Tjantings come in a number of forms and sizes. There are tjantings with one, two and three spouts. Traditionally crafts people made their own tjantings using a wooden handle and small metal, bone or stone spout.

You can also buy electric tjantings. These heat up the wax so you do not need a pot to melt it.

Using stamps (tjaps)

Wax can be applied using a stamp. This can be used to produce repeat patterns.

The printing blocks used to apply wax are called **tjaps**. Cork, wood and even cut potatoes can be used to make a tjap.

You can make your own tjap by gluing a flat piece of wood onto a handle.

The design can be produced using string glued to the flat surface, cardboard or corrugated card.

You can experiment with different materials to produce the pattern on your tjap.

When using hot wax it is important to ensure that the wax is hot enough to soak into the fabric.

 Wear safety gloves and protective clothing when using hot wax

Brushing

Wax can be applied directly onto fabric using a brush. Very interesting effects can be achieved by varying the type of brush. Traditional designs can be achieved by stretching the fabric, then painting both sides with wax using a decorator's brush. When the wax has solidified, scratch off a design using a blunt needle, fork or screwdriver. Remember to scratch off the wax right down to the fabric. Turn the fabric over and scratch off the design on the other side. Ensure that no wax remains where you want the fabric to receive colour.

Dripping

Wax can be applied to fabric by dripping it using a stick, tjanting or brush. The height from which you drip the wax will alter the finished effect, as will the tool that you use, how much wax you drip and how random the drips are.

Crackling

Crackling is caused when the brittle wax cracks, allowing dye to reach the fabric. You can create a traditional crackling effect by covering the fabric with wax. Once it has dried, crumple it in your hands. You can also crack the brittle wax in other ways. By folding the fabric very interesting results can be obtained. Different waxes produce different effects. You can put the coated fabric into the fridge or freezer to alter the brittleness of the wax and change the finished effect of the fabric.

To remove the wax from the fabric, first scrape away whatever you can, then sandwich the fabric between several sheets of absorbent paper. A hot iron is used to melt the wax, which is then absorbed by the paper. Finally the fabric is washed.

Gutta

Gutta is an alternative to wax. It is a gum that is painted directly onto the fabric. You cannot get the same effects as with wax, but gutta is safe and easy to use. You can get colourless gutta or coloured gutta. Gold and silver gutta are popular in Indian textile design.

The oldest known batik dates from when the pharaohs ruled Egypt. In Indonesia, batik textiles were sometimes used as money. Batiks had important ritual significance and would be used to cure illness and prevent damage by evil spirits. In Indo-China fine geometric patterns were produced with an iron pen.

Activity 62

Try to investigate any traditional influences that your class and their families have about batik. Ask parents and grandparents if they know of any particular design or cultural uses of batik. Share your findings with your class.

Silk Painting

As well as dyeing the fabric by immersing it in a dye bath, you can use **resist dye painting**. Dye or coloured fabric paint (silk paint) is applied by using a brush within a resist outline. Gutta is the resist used to make the outline.

If the fabric is moistened before applying the colours, softer shades can be obtained.

1 Put the silk on the frame.

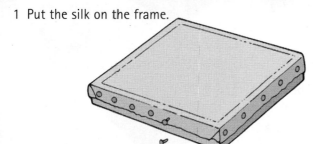

2 Outline your design with gutta. To check there are no breaks in the gutta, hold up to the light.

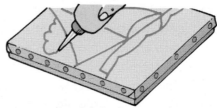

3 Use a brush to paint on the dyes – work quickly before the paint dries.

4 Dry fabric. Remove the gutta and fix the paint.

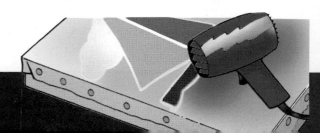

Activity 63

Design and produce a wax-resist fabric sample based on the theme 'cold'. Think about snow, icebergs, snowflakes and frozen leaves. Choose your colours and shapes carefully to reflect the theme.

Chemical resists

This type of resist technique uses a wide range of chemical compounds to prevent colour from bonding with the fabric. Chemical resists are popular on cellulose-based fabrics, silk and wools.

Patchwork

Patchwork consists of joining small pieces of fabric together. Usually the pieces of fabric are first cut into regular geometric shapes.

The Inuit Indians used patchwork to decorate their garments. They would often replace a section of a coat with fur patches. The Crusaders in the eleventh century returned with fancy, colourful banners made by patching geometric shapes of bright fabric together. For centuries, the English monarchs surrounded themselves with patchwork textile products – Queen Elizabeth I even had patchwork dresses. In Victorian times, squares and hexagons were added to plain clothing to decorate it. The early settlers in America had to import fabrics from thousands of miles away. This made fabrics very expensive. People tried to make the best use of every small fragment of fabric, and would patch worn-out garments. This led to some wonderful patchwork textile products, and the designs that were developed are still used today.

There are four main varieties of patchwork:

Crazy, in which small pieces of fabric are put together without apparent plan, or attempt to produce a design. Care needs to be taken to place the fabric pieces according to their shape. This type of patchwork is very economical as it can use up every single piece of fabric. The finished product is similar to crazy paving. Silk, velvet, linen and cotton can all be used, but it is normal to use one type of fabric.

Crazy patchwork looks best where fewer than one-third of the patches contain a pattern of their own. Take care when you choose your colours.

Strip, in which rectangles are joined into long strips of fabric, which can then be put together to make a piece of cloth. The effect is half way between crazy patchwork and all-over patchwork. All the pieces must be of the same type of fabric. Strip patchwork is usually made from rectangles 5–8 cm wide.

All-over. Most English patchwork is of this type, particularly patchwork from Victorian times. Geometric shapes are used and are joined without leaving gaps to spoil the pattern. Whilst the geometric pattern is kept regular, plain and patterned patches of every colour may appear in the same piece of patchwork. All-over patchwork and appliqué can be hard to tell apart. Technically, the difference is that appliqué is made with embroidery stitches and patchwork with plain hand or machine stitches. The geometric shapes (such as squares, rectangles, hexagons, diamonds and triangles) are usually cut out using paper or metal templates to ensure that the pieces are of an even size, otherwise they will not fit together properly.

American block, made in a series of small squares. Each square, called a block, is finished separately. To make the complete textile product, the joined blocks are then sewn together according to a strict pattern, and appliquéd onto a backing cloth, traditionally quilted. The appliqué often takes the form of attractive embroidery stitches that add further decoration to the joined blocks. There are many traditional designs of American block patchwork. Some of them have special significance. Even the pattern of the quilting is carefully selected to match the overall design of the patchwork. It used to be quite normal for several people to work together to finish a quilt large enough for a big bed.

Appliqué

The word appliqué means applied work. Appliqué refers to the process of adding one or more pieces of fabric onto a fabric background. Appliqué is a variation on patchwork, but the cut-outs are joined to a background rather than being joined to each other. By using appliqué it is possible to decorate and add colour and shape to the product. It is an ancient craft. Eskimos appliqué tiny squares of brightly coloured leather into geometric patterns on their boots and coats.

Appliqué can be used to decorate almost any textile product. Eye-catching designs can easily be achieved. Appliqué is ideal for making things for children as brightly coloured shapes can be applied to playmats, toys, cot covers and wall hangings. By inserting a piece of wadding or stuffing behind the fabric, wonderful three-dimensional effects can be achieved.

Before you can produce an appliqué, you need to design simplified shapes for the applied fabric. Christmas and birthday cards are a valuable source of inspiration, or you can produce your own simplified designs. When you design your appliqué, refer to the section of the book on simplification of shapes (see pages 77–8). Once you have mastered the technique you will be able to add motifs and logos.

Appliqué can be used to enhance the properties of fabric, for example to improve thermal resistance. Appliqué can be achieved by hand sewing, by using a sewing machine, or by bonding.

Traditionally appliqué is achieved by using satin stitch, but all sorts of interesting effects can be achieved by using other types of stitching. Appliqué can also be achieved by using iron-on fabrics, sequins and small beads. Reverse appliqué is achieved by producing two layers and then cutting out areas of the top layer.

It is important to choose fabrics for appliqué that have similar care requirements to the background. This means ensuring that the characteristics of fabric, for example washing and ironing, are similar.

Activity 64

Design and make an appliqué tablemat on the theme of 'heat'. Think about images like the Sun, fire, desert and volcanoes. Remember to choose colours and textures carefully to suit the theme.

Design and make an appliqué tablemat on the theme of 'heat'. Your tablemat should be attractive to a young child. Think about images like the Sun, fire, desert and volcanoes. Remember to choose colours and textures carefully to suit the theme.

Design and make a set of appliqué tablemats on the theme of 'heat'. Your tablemats should be attractive to a young child. Think about images like the Sun, fire, desert and volcanoes alongside the textures and colours in a plate of food. How can the tablemat and plate of food work together to reflect the theme? How can the tablemats work together to tell a story and create a mood? Remember to choose carefully and position well your chosen colours, textures and fabric properties to suit the theme.

Hand appliqué

Hand appliqué is achieved by stitching by hand the edges of the applied fabric. It is best to keep designs simple, as you will have to turn the edges to the wrong side to prevent your applied design from fraying. Mark the shape you require on the back of the fabric to be applied and then add a one-centimetre edge to fold over. Cut out the shape. Turn over the edge and tack. Now apply your design to the base fabric. You can use embroidery stitches to enhance the design.

Hand appliqué is ideal for thicker fabrics that will not fit through the sewing machine.

Machine appliqué

Machine appliqué is easier than hand appliqué because you do not need to turn the edges. You can use a zigzag stitch or close satin stitch to prevent fraying. If the fabric you are applying is starchy or thin you should use a backing fabric first. You can, however, only use fabrics that will fit through the sewing machine.

Bonded appliqué

Bonded appliqué does not use stitches. The applied fabric is bonded to the backing fabric by using iron-on tape or adhesives.

Cultural influences

The Egyptians used appliqué 3000 years ago. Tutankhamun's tomb contained an appliqué collar. Men can still be seen making appliqués in old Cairo. Traditionally, they were made into ceremonial tents. The Inuit Indians also made appliqué clothing. In India and Pakistan appliqués were traditionally used at celebrations, such as weddings. It was also common to decorate animals with appliqué-decorated collars and coats. In Africa appliqué designs were used to show the chief's status and power. Hawaiian people create appliqué designs based upon their lush vegetation. Vietnamese textiles often incorporate intricate appliquéd spirals.

Quilting

Quilting involves sandwiching a layer of wadding between two or more layers of fabric and sewing the layers together. It is possible to buy fabrics which are already quilted. Traditionally, people would get together for communal quilting sessions. There were also travelling quilt-makers, who would move from farm to farm in remote areas. Quilting is one of the best ways to insulate fabric. The wadding traps air between the two layers of fabric, and this helps to retain heat. Interesting effects can also be achieved by stitching the layers to form a decorative pattern.

The simplest kind of quilting is **tied**, sometimes called **tufted quilting**. One or more strands of thread are taken through the fabric twice and tied in knots at regular intervals.

It is more common, however, to use stitching than tied quilting. Quilting is easier to achieve on fabrics which are not stretchy.

For more on cultural influences see pages 99–105.

Quilting by hand

First sandwich the layers together. Then secure the sewing thread on the wrong side of the fabric. When you push the needle through the fabric, try to ensure that it is straight and not at an angle. If the needle is not straight, the fabric will pucker.

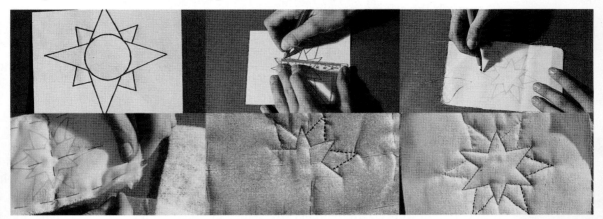

Quilting by machine

You can use the sewing machine to quilt. Machine quilting has obvious advantages over hand quilting. It is quicker, stitches are even, and you can quilt a wider range of materials. Synthetic fabrics are easier to sew using the sewing machine than by hand. Machine quilting does, however, have its drawbacks. It is difficult to quilt large items using a machine, and it is not suited to intricate designs, although these can be achieved by free machining using the special foot.

Quilting is achieved by using either straight stitch or narrow zigzag stitch. Traditional quilting uses straight parallel lines of stitching in different directions. You must ensure that your stitching is straight if you want to achieve traditional quilting. Interesting effects can be achieved, however, by using curve stitching. Most sewing machines are supplied with a special quilting foot. The quilting foot guides the fabrics through a metal bar. This helps to achieve evenly placed lines of stitching.

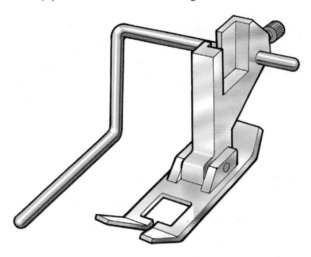

Closely woven fabrics are best for machine quilting. Be careful when machine quilting that your tacking stitches do not get caught in the machine stitching.

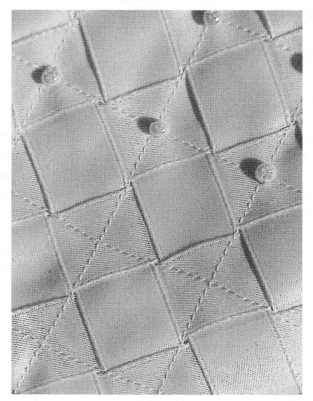

Activity 65

Design and make a simple cushion using African, Chinese or Indian textiles for inspiration. Use at least one technique described in the book to decorate your design.

Design and make a simple cushion incorporating images from African, Chinese or Indian textiles. Use at least two of the techniques described in the book to decorate your cushion.

Research at least one traditional textile design from Africa, China, South America, Pakistan or India. Design and make a cushion using a range of techniques described in the book.

Recycling

Caring for the environment and recycling have become more wide-spread in recent years. Taking a textile product or piece of fabric and changing its original appearance can give it a new lease of life, especially when it is made into something useful. One way of recycling textiles is to add colour and decoration to an existing product using dyes, printing or appliqué. Another way of making environmentally friendly products is by the use of ragwork.

Ragwork

Ragwork uses recycled materials to make new textile products. It can transform old, worn-out fabrics into a new, useful textile product. Ragwork is a traditional textile craft that almost disappeared, but is now making a comeback in the fashion and interior design world. Ragwork is environmentally friendly because it uses recycled materials.

Modern ragwork techniques come from traditional rug-making. Some ragwork rugs have lasted hundreds of years. Six different techniques are used in ragwork:

- **Knitting** – strips of fabric can be knitted together by using the strips like yarn.
- **Hooking** – strips of fabric are hooked through a hessian tapestry canvas or open-weave fabric and then looped back through. To create a pile surface, the loops are then sheared off.
- **Prodding** – traditionally, wool cuttings were pushed through an open weave backing fabric.
- **Braiding** – braiding was popular in North America. Three strips of fabric are braided or plaited together and then machine or hand stitched. They can then be wound into circular shapes or rectangular rugs.
- **Crochet** – strips of fabric are crocheted together in the same way as you would crochet wool.
- **Wrapping** – thin strips of fabric are bound together with threads. Wire is often used to produce beautiful sculptured jewellery.

Textile Techniques from Around the World

The designs that we use to adorn modern textiles have evolved over the centuries. They are influenced by tradition and culture from around the world. There are four main categories of textile design from around the world:

1 **Simple** geometric **shapes** such as lines, spirals, squares and curves.
2 **Natural ornament**, where the designer has taken inspiration from the natural world, such as flowers and animals.
3 **Structural designs** taken from buildings and the made world, such as brickwork and tile patterns.
4 **Symbolic designs** including mystical creatures, water drops and religious symbols.

Activity 66

Find one design from each of the four categories that can be used to study influences on textile designs from around the world.

Use of Textiles Around the World

Inuits

With a mean annual temperature below minus 10 °C in their homeland, Inuits' clothing has to be warm. Decoration is added traditionally by mixing textures and shearing the fabric of threads. Inuit clothing was also decorated using patchwork, decorative margins and carved bone pendants. Inuits embellished the seams of their clothing using stitching and different coloured bands of leather and fur. They would also replace sections of the garment with decorative units. To provide protection from the cold, fabric is often layered, and this also provides a unique design feature. The pendants added to the base of garments provided both decoration and added weight, preventing the garments from blowing up in the wind.

Activity 67

Investigate garments worn in cold climates. How does the functioning of the garment affect the design? How has garment design for cold climates affected today's fashion clothing?

Romania

Romanian textiles were influenced significantly by the Romans who occupied the land from AD 106 to AD 217, hence <u>Roman</u>ia. Embroidered sheepskin coats are traditional in Romania. Romanian textile designs are often reminiscent of the designs the Romans put on their stonework columns. Traditional Romanian textiles were also embroidered with summer flowers and designs reflecting nature. When it rained, people would often turn their coats inside out to protect the bright designs. Early Romanian designers used a wide range of bright colours in their textile products, but were especially fond of reds. The colours were produced using natural dyes. The plants used to make these dyes were planted according to the stars. Fabric dying could only take place when the crafts people were healthy and free from worry.

You can learn much about the application of pattern, colour and rhythm by studying Romanian textiles. Patterns are usually bold and colourful and are created on white backgrounds. Secondary patterns are added to fill the spaces between the main patterns.

Activity 68

Investigate how textile designers have copied the world around us (flowers, animals, the weather) in textile designs.

Egypt

Egyptian textile designs were developed over 3000 years. Similar mystical images appear time and time again. The Egyptians used embroidery and weaving to produce large quantities of textile products. During the 31 years that Rameses III was in power, it is believed that 37 882 textile products were made to be given to the gods. In addition, yards of linen are needed to mummify a body.

In ancient Egypt, material was difficult to dye. Colour was added using beads, jewels and flowers and by painting directly onto fabric. Traditional designs were often painted onto the mummy. Appliqué was used in early Egypt, where boats travelled up and down the Nile with bold appliqué designs on their sails.

Later, the Coptic Christians in Egypt embroidered fine tapestry medallions on their tunics. When the Arabs invaded Egypt in AD 642, a lack of time to complete their embroidery forced the Christians to sew circular and square pieces of fabric onto their garments. Today's ecclesiastical vestments are believed to originate from this time.

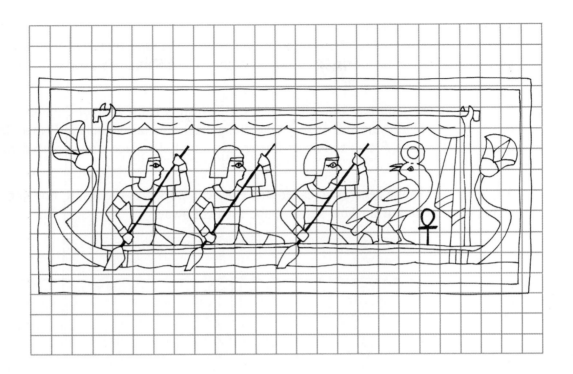

Greece

Greece was located in the middle of the great sea routes of the Middle Ages. It was a place where Christianity and Islam met, a place where West meets East. As a result, its textile designs were often mythological in character. Double-headed eagles and mythological animals were common. Other designs came from Italy and the Far East. Traditionally, Greek textile design reflects simple geometric patterns. Greek textile designers were often economical with their time and effort. Where many layers of clothing were worn, only the parts that showed, such as hems and cuffs, incorporated designs. Bed covers and furniture would only be worked where the design would be seen.

France

In France, the Bayeux tapestry is of great importance. The tapestry is 231 feet long, and was embroidered to commemorate the Norman victory in the Battle of Hastings in 1066. It was probably embroidered by men.

One of the most important times in French textile history is the time of Cardinal Richelieu. He was Minister to Louis XIII. At that time, Italian lace was fashionable in France. To encourage lace work in France, Richelieu imposed heavy taxes on Italian lace, and imported lace workers from Venice.

A new form of fabric decoration called **Richelieu cut work** was the result: fine linen was embroidered with button-hole stitches, and then cut away.

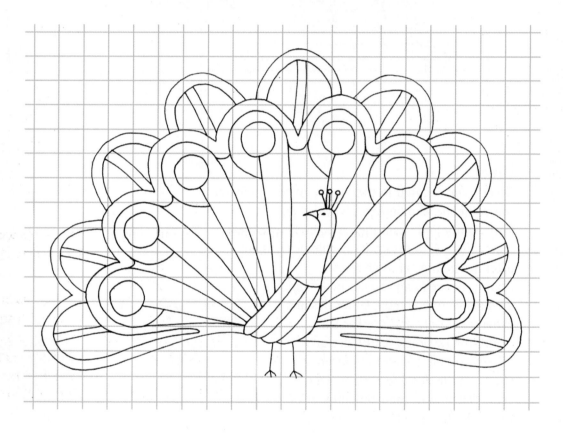

India and Pakistan

In India, textile design is an ancient art more than 4000 years old. Embroidery needles dating from 2300 BC have been discovered on the Indian sub-continent. As in dance, where every gesture stands for a concept or myth, colour has an immense significance in Indian textiles. Lime green means early summer, red brings good fortune and saffron means spring. In Indian textiles even white is broken down into five tones: ivory white, jasmine white, conch white, white of the August moon, and white August clouds when rain is spent. Indian and Pakistani textiles are often bright in colour. They aim to shine and glitter. Many textile products incorporate small mirrors and gold and silver thread.

Animals, both real and imaginary, have social and symbolic importance. Muslim textiles are highly stylised as the Koran forbids the depiction of human and animal forms.

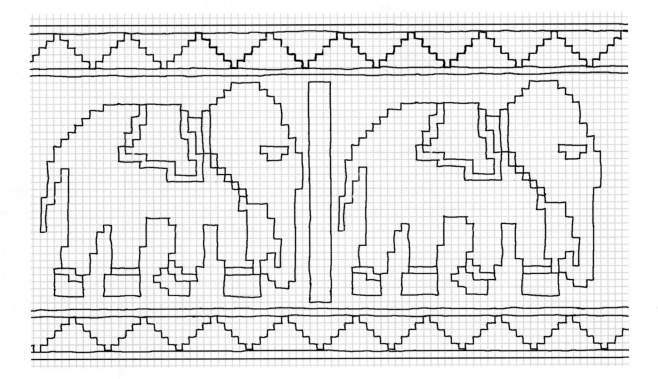

Indian textiles often incorporate very formalised representations of flowers, birds and animals. The designs are highly stylised and use glorious colours. The display of embroidery is of great importance at weddings.

There is an ancient Indian legend. It says that once upon a time, people did not wear any clothes because they did not know how to weave the textiles. A young child with sharp eyes sat quietly by a river and watched the waves and ripples on the surface. She looked up at the trees and she noticed the patterns of interwoven branches and leaves. The god Matai rewarded the child by teaching her how to weave. The child used the patterns she had seen in nature to embroider beautiful clothes for her friends. Some of her designs turned into butterflies and can be seen on the markings of butterfly wings.

Africa

African textiles incorporate some of the best examples of resist dying and embroidered spirals, triangles, squares and circles. Textile designs play an important part in ritual and ceremony. African textiles also include glorious, vibrant, heavily patterned textiles influenced by the appliquéd and embroidered flags of the Asafo warriers. They range from decorative, abstract images to the geometric patterns of the Shoowa tribe of Zaire.

Traditionally, only very rich people in Africa wore heavily embroidered full-length robes, called **warramba**. The garment was a symbol of social status and was handed down from generation to generation.

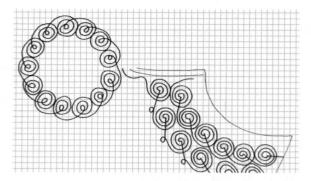

The arrival of the sewing machine made embroidery available and affordable to all Africans. Traders in Nigeria and Gambia would sit in the street with their machines and decorate garments to order. They would stick thick thread that was much too thick to fit into the bobbin onto the surface of the fabric to achieve fascinating designs. Fabrics would be woven with raffia and be decorated with maze-like patterns. Earthy colours are popular in African textiles.

South America

In the late 1600s the people of South America changed designs that had been used in body painting and used them for textile and cloth painting. Stylised animals and geometric motifs were popular.

China

Textiles have a tradition going back 4000 years in China. Until the Chinese Revolution in 1947, social rank was indicated by what people wore. There were 12 symbols used in China's textiles. Each of these symbols represented a concept: for example, clouds represented heaven and mountains represented the Earth. Only the Emperor, who was a god between heaven and his people, could wear all 12.

Iran

Iranian art was produced for the gods. Delicate designs were made, even in places that would never be seen. In desert land with hot sun, designs would reflect beautiful, shady gardens with running water. Iran (formerly Persia) is famous for rugs, hence Persian rugs. The nomadic tribesmen would decorate their tents, horses and camels with beautiful textile products. Colour was important too: it was used to protect the owner from evil.

Activity 69

Recycle a piece of clothing by adding to or modifying it.

Test

1. What are primary colours?
2. What are dyes and what are the differences between natural and synthetic dyes?
3. List six words that can be used to describe fabric texture.
4. Describe one way of adding texture to fabric.
5. Why is mathematics important in textiles design and manufacture?
6. Define the following terms: focal point, stripes, borders, squares, repeat patterns.
7. Describe the process of block printing.
8. How are stencils used to create textile designs?
9. What is screen printing?
10. Describe four techniques for direct application of designs onto textiles.
11. What is tie and dye and what special effects can be achieved using tie and dye?
12. What is batik and what special effects can be achieved using batik?
13. Where did the following techniques originate: patchwork, appliqué.
14. Describe traditional textile products from three of the following countries: Romania, Egypt, Greece, Africa, India and Pakistan, China.

Section 4

Structures

Making Three-Dimensional Structures from Fabric

Most textile products are not flat; they are three-dimensional. Three-dimensional products are created by making structures. These structures enable tents to fit their frames and clothing to fit around a person. Most fabrics are soft and flexible, but they must be cut and joined to produce the right structure. The structures must be the right shape and strength. Starch, wire and layers can be used to add strength to the structures.

In this section we will explore three-dimensional structures and how they are created by using different pieces of fabric.

Before you can produce quality textile products by using structures, you need to understand how people interact with the textile products they use. The name given to the study of the function of objects and how people use them is **ergonomics**. *Ergonomics* comes from the Greek words *ergon* (work) and *nomos* (law). To understand ergonomics you need to study people, what they do and how big or small they are. Bear in mind that there is no such thing as an average person. We are all different sizes and shapes. When designers study our size and shape they collect data. The name given to this is **anthropometrics**. Without anthropometrics, our clothes and textile products would be uncomfortable and difficult to use.

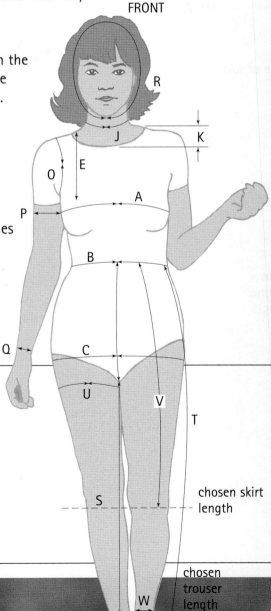

FRONT

Anthropometrics

Let us explore the data that are needed to produce clothing.

There are lots of measurements we can take:

A chest or bust
B waist
C hips
D shoulder to shoulder
E neck to underarm
F waist to underarm
G shoulder to base of garment
H back of neck to lower edge
I back of neck to waist

chosen skirt length

chosen trouser length

Anthropometrical measurements are vital to designers. Once they have the measurements, they can decide how loose or tight the garment will be, how long or short it will be and how it will be shaped to fit the body.

If the garment is a one-off, it will be made to fit a particular person. For most of us, our clothes are made in large numbers and are sized to suit an average person. To help, garments are usually made in small, medium and large sizes or in a range of predetermined sizes, called **standard sizes**. The charts below shows standard sizes for women, with examples for boys and men. All measurements are in centimetres.

Women

Size	8	10	12	14	16
Bust (A)	80	83	87	92	97
Waist (B)	61	64	67	71	76
Hips (C)	85	88	92	97	102
Back (I)	40	40.5	41.5	2	42.5

Boys/Men

Size	Boys' size 12	16	Men's 34
Chest (A)	76	85	87
Waist (B)	66	71	71
Hips (C)	79	87	89
Neck (J)	33	35.5	35.5

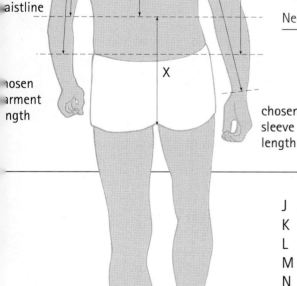

BACK

Top of spine

waistline

chosen garment length

chosen sleeve length

Taking measurements from comfortable clothes is easier than measuring your body.

J around neck
K neckline depth
L neck width
M shoulder depth
N neck to sleeve edge
O around arm hole
P upper arm width
Q wrist

R around face
S inside leg
T outside leg
U thigh measurement
V skirt length
W ankle
X crotch
Y head size for hats.

Activity 70

Fashion and garment function affect the size of our clothing. For example, it may be fashionable to have baggy clothing, tight clothing, padded shoulders, or straight or flared trousers that fit on our hips or waist. Sports clothes are often tight and streamlined. Compare the measurements of your body with the measurements of your clothing. Where do they differ, and why?

Compare the measurements of your body with the measurements of your clothing. Under the headings of **fashion**, **free movement** and **function**, state where the measurements differ and why.

Compare the measurements and shape of your body with the measurements and shape of your clothing. Under the headings of **fashion**, **free movement** and **function**, state where the measurements and shapes differ and why. Illustrate your findings with drawings and notes.

Types of Structure

There are two types of structure: **frame** (for example, a spider's web) and **shell** (for example, the honeycomb in a beehive) structures. Most textile products, including clothing, are made using shell structures. The shape of the garment gives it its strength. Seams, pattern structure and stitching all add extra support and ensure that the product looks and functions as designed.

You must consider the structure of both product and fabric when designing textile products. Refer back to Section One of the book, which explores fabric construction, before you design a three-dimensional textile product.

To shape garments to fit our bodies, designers have to think carefully about the way the garment is structured. Flat fabric has to be shaped to fit our rounded bodies by using cutting and darts. We will explore this in more detail later. The exceptions to this are saris, wraps and headscarves, which are single pieces of fabric wound around the body to form a structure of pleats and folds.

There are three ways to give textile products the structure and form they must have to function as the designer intends:
- produce three-dimensional fabric by knitting or moulding
- cut and shape the fabric by careful use of pattern pieces and seams
- use construction techniques like darts, pleats and tucks to remove excess fabric and create shape and form.

Activity 71

Change the shape of a flat piece of fabric using darts, pleats, gathers or tucks.

Knitting and moulding

Using computer-controlled knitting machines, manufacturers can knit in three dimensions. It is also possible to hand knit in three dimensions, using a frame or hoop. Three-dimensional knitting is used to produce a wide range of textile products, from car seat covers to clothing. Products made this way have the advantage of having no seams. This saves cost as the product takes less time to manufacture. Seams are the weakest part of the product; seamless products are, therefore, stronger.

Hats are often moulded into shape. Felt hats are made by pressing the raw fibres into a mould. New non-woven fabrics and rubber are used by textile designers in pre-formed shapes.

Pattern design

Deciding how many pieces of fabric a garment will be made from is a vital part of the designer's role. Pattern pieces can be shaped to give textile products form and to change the style of the garment. Simple changes to the shape and size of the pieces can have a dramatic effect on the finished product. Manufacturers like to reduce the number of pieces used, as it costs money to join them together.

Using Patterns

Of course, designers know where to start. There are basic shapes that form the building blocks for garments and other textile products. The designer can modify patterns to create interesting and functional designs. The pattern pieces shown are the building blocks for trousers, skirts, shirts and jackets. Patterns can also be made by what is called **disassembly** of existing clothing. This means taking items apart by undoing the seams carefully so that the component parts can be laid out.

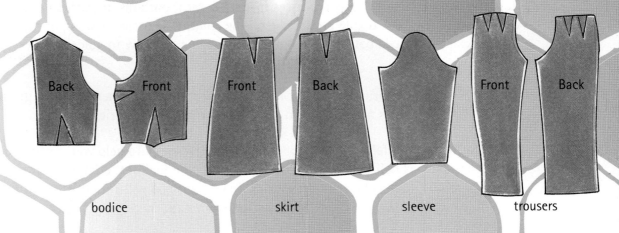

bodice   skirt   sleeve   trousers

Producing original patterns is a difficult and complicated process. The best way to design a garment is to start with an existing paper pattern that is similar to what you want and then to modify it to suit your design ideas.

It is easy to modify and adapt patterns by adding and subtracting features. You can also try out your patterns in paper, by using an old sheet or in calico before you make the real product.

Activity 72

Choose a garment you like to wear. Look at the garment and work out how many pieces it is made from. Draw the shape of each piece. Look at the label. Does it say where the garment was made? What does it say about the type of fabric used?

Choose a blouse or shirt you like to wear. Look at the garment and work out how many pieces it is made from. Draw the pieces to scale and show how they have been cut from the fabric, remembering to indicate the grain of the fabric. What types of stitches have been used to join the pieces together?

Choose three garments you like to wear. One garment should be a shirt or blouse, one a pair of trousers or a skirt and the third a fashion accessory. Look at each garment in turn and work out how many pieces each is made from. How do the garment pieces differ? How have they been joined together? Draw the pieces to scale and show how they have been cut from the fabric, remembering to indicate the grain of the fabric.

Cutting out

Once you have a pattern, the next step is to work out how to cut it out of the fabric. You should place your pattern pieces carefully on the fabric, so that as little material as possible is wasted. The name given to this is **lay planning**. Computers are used in industry to do this.

Unfortunately, it is not as easy as just laying the pattern pieces onto the fabric in any direction. This is due to the grain of the fabric. Section Two of this book explored grain in fabric resulting from the weaving and knitting processes (page 28). Most patterns are designed to fit so that the vertical sections of the textile product lie on the lengthwise grain, or warp, of the fabric. Commercially produced pattern pieces often have a line or arrow to guide users.

Activity 73

Cut one piece of fabric diagonally across the grain and another with the grain. See what the differences are when you stretch and shape the fabric.

It is usual to fold the fabric and to cut on a double thickness. To help you, cutting patterns are usually designed as half pieces that can be placed on the fold of the fabric or as pattern pieces that require two identical pieces like sleeves. This means you will cut out the two pieces at once. It is helpful to lay the large pieces on the fabric first, as close as you can, and then fit the smaller pieces around them.

Some fabrics are harder to fit into the pattern than others. This is because they have **nap**, a **pile** or a **printed pattern**. You will need to think carefully about cutting fabric with a printed pattern as you may want to line up the pattern at the seams. Fabrics with nap and pile often look different if held different ways up. You will need to ensure that each piece is cut the right way up or the finished product could look odd.

Construction Techniques

Darts, tucks and pleats all work on the principle that, if excess fabric is removed from one place, the textile product can be shaped to suit its purpose. If you think about a blouse or shirt it must start at the collar, go out to fit our shoulders, be shaped to fit our chest and come in to fit our waist, not forgetting that we need room to move our arms without splitting the seams. We also have to be able to remove the garment.

Joining pieces of fabric together to create structures

There are two ways you can join fabric together: **permanently** or **temporarily**.

Temporary fastenings are used when you wish to open up or take apart a join. Permanent fastenings are used to assemble the pieces into the finished textile product. Before you choose an appropriate fastening, you need to consider how strong the joint needs to be.

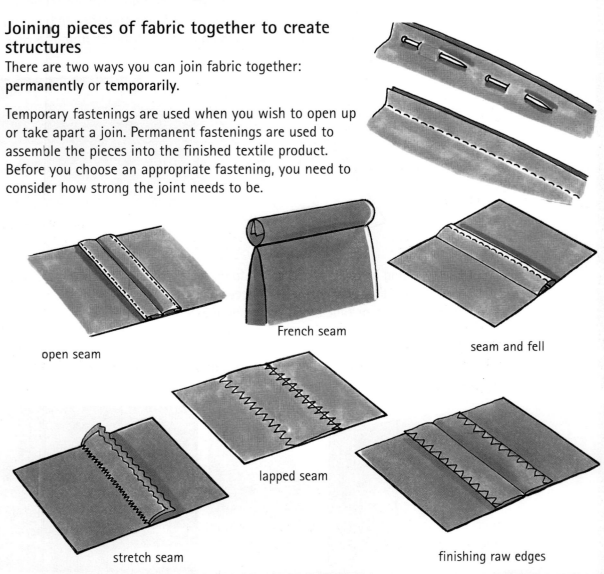

open seam

French seam

seam and fell

lapped seam

stretch seam

finishing raw edges

Pins and tacking stitches are used to hold fabric pieces temporarily before stitching. Always check to ensure that pins are free from rust before you use them. If you do not, they will mark the fabric. There are two ways to sew your fabric pieces together: by **hand** or by **machine**.

A seam is a line of stitches joining two or more pieces of fabric. The seam itself will alter the properties of the fabric. When designing textile products care should be taken to choose both the position of the seams and the type of seam. For example, you must use small zigzag stitching on stretchable fabric or the seam will prevent the fabric from stretching.

There is a wide range of seams that you can choose from. You should choose the best seam for the fabric and textile product you are making. Use the following information to help you choose the type of seam best suited to your product.

Flat seam

This is the most common and simplest method of joining two pieces of fabric. Flat seams are easy to produce. Place the right sides of the pieces of fabric together and pin in place. Sew 10 to 20mm in from the edge, keeping the stitching an even distance from the edge of the fabric. Open up the edges and press flat.

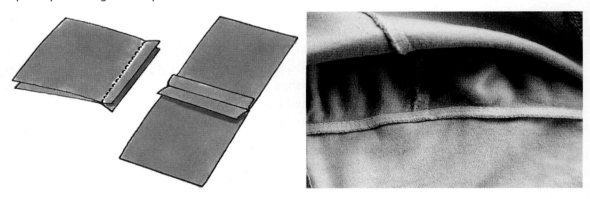

Sometimes binding or tape is used to reinforce the seam. This is called a **taped seam**. To achieve a taped seam, start by placing the two pieces of fabric together with the right sides facing and pin and tack binding or tape along the seam line. Stitch together carefully.

Piped seam

Piping is a popular method of fabric decoration, particularly for home furnishing. Piped seams can be corded or soft.

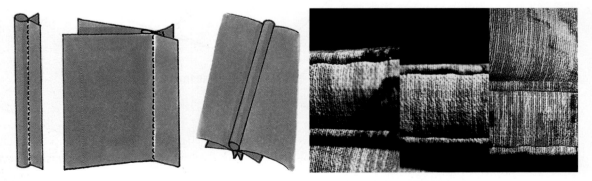

French seam

French seams are used on fine fabrics that are likely to fray. Unlike plain seams, where you start by putting the fabric together on the right side, for French seams the fabric is first placed together on the wrong side. Stitch about 10 mm from the edge and then trim both seams to about 4 mm. Now fold the fabric so the right sides are together and pin and stitch 5 mm from the edge.

Overlaid seam

Overlaid seams are sometimes referred to as **lapped seams**. They are often used on gathered, pleated or tucked fabric. They are made by folding the fabric or inserting a piece of different fabric.

Seam and fell

This type of seam is used to give strength. Tents and furniture fabrics are often stitched this way. Sometimes a contrasting coloured thread is used to add a design feature. Place the fabric with the wrong sides together and pin and stitch about 15 mm from the edge. One side of the fabric seam is then cut back, leaving about 5 mm. The wider seam is then folded, pressed and stitched.

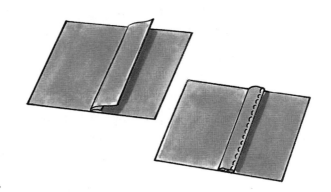

Finishing the Edges of Fabric

It is important to ensure that the edges of your textile product are finished. Edges can be finished using hems, bindings and facings.

Hems

A hem is simply a stitched or glued fold in the fabric turned to the wrong side. Hems are versatile as they are simple to make.

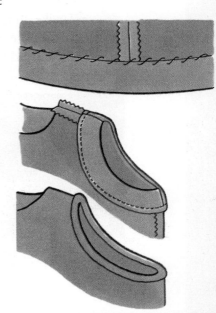

Facings

Facings are pieces of fabric used to tidy and finish raw edges. They are attached to the wrong side and are invisible on the right side of the fabric.

Bindings

Bindings can be seen on both sides of the fabric. The binding covers the edge of the fabric. They can be used as attractive design features.

Other techniques

Whenever you wish to sew curved seams, you will need to **notch** or **clip** the seam. This enables the fabric to bend.

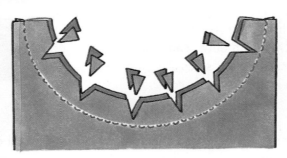
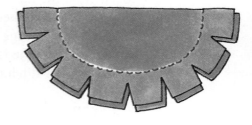

Changing the Shape of Fabric

There are a number of ways to alter the shape of a textile product. **Tucks** and **pleats**, **gathering** and **darts** are the most common.

Tucks, darts and pleats are important ways of styling textile products.

Pleats

Pleats are commonly used on waistbands and hips of trousers and skirts. Sometimes waistbands contain over three times the amount of fabric needed to fit around the waist. Without pleats in clothing we would not be able to sit down or move freely. There are four different types of pleat:

- **Knife pleats** are sharp folds facing in the same direction. They form a concertina effect.
- **Box pleats** have two knife pleats facing away from each other on the right side of the fabric. This produces a box shape.
- **Inverted pleats** are the opposite of box pleats. Two knife pleats meet together on the right side of the fabric.
- Unlike all the other pleats, **kick pleats** start partway down a garment and are made by adding a separate piece of fabric. Designers often use them to allow extra leg movement in tight skirts.

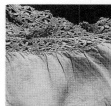

Tucks

A tuck is simply a fold in the fabric, held in place using stitching. There are four different types of tuck:

1 **Pin tucks** – a very attractive effect can be achieved with pin tucks. These are simply very small seams stitched into the fabric at regular intervals, with the small tucks pressed in the direction required on the right side of the garment. Pin tucks are often used on shirts and blouses instead of gathers and darts.

2 **Spaced tucks** – these have a flat space between each tuck.

3 **Blind tucks** – these meet or overlap each other.

4 **Decorative tucks** include
   - **piped tucks**: the tuck is formed over a piece of card or wire
   - **cross tucks**: where both horizontal and vertical tucks are used for decoration
   - **shell tucks**: shell shapes are formed in the fabric by forming a tuck and overstitching.

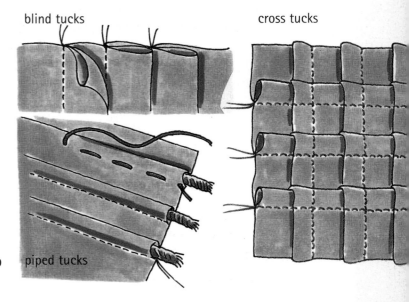

blind tucks

cross tucks

piped tucks

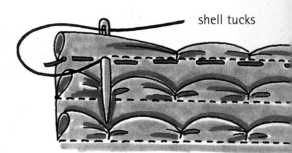

shell tucks

Gathering

Gathering is similar to tucks and pleats. It is, in effect, lots of small tucks. Gathering is usually achieved by inserting gathering threads by hand or by machine and then pulling them up to achieve the desired effect. Gathering is used to fit longer edges to short edges.

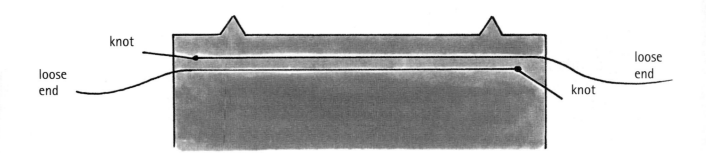

knot

loose end

loose end

knot

Darts

Darts are folds of fabric which end in a point. They are used to change the shape of a product. They are often used to achieve close-fitting clothes. There are two main types of dart: **single-point** and **double-point** darts. Single-point darts start at a seam line and taper away to nothing. Double-point darts have a point at each end and expand in the centre. They usually occur in the middle of the fabric. Darts can be used to add strength and form. The dart can be made with straight or curved lines. Each method achieves a different contour in the garment. Curved-line darts are often referred to as **shaped** or **contour** darts.

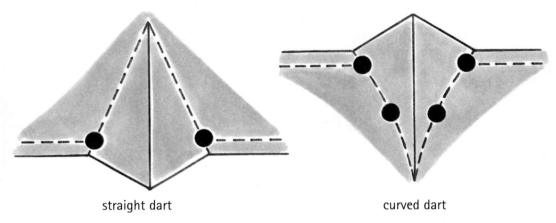

straight dart   curved dart

Activity 74

Look at the darts shown in the pictures. Find out how darts are used in the clothing you and your friends are wearing. Record them using sketches and notes in your books.

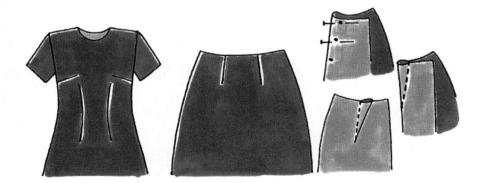

Bands and belts

Bands and belts are often used to shape textile products. The band effect can be achieved in a number of different ways. Often bands are cut in contrasting fabric which can be stitched into place.

Remember to stitch stretch fabrics loosely or you will remove the stretch.

Temporary Fastenings

There is a wide range of temporary fastenings for use in textile items. You will need to consider carefully the requirements of your textile product before selecting the most appropriate fastening. Fastenings can be used for decorating a textile product, as well as for function. When selecting the correct fastener, you must consider cost, appearance and how firmly you need the materials to fix. Does the fastener need to be washable? How easy should it be to open and close? How strong does the fastening need to be?

Fastener	How easy to use	Strength	Cost	Ease of fitting
Buttons	★★	★★★	★★	★★★
Zips	★★★	★★★★	★★★	★★★
Velcro	★★★★	★★★	★★★	★★
Hook and Eyes	★★	★	★★	★★
Frog and Toggles	★★★	★★	★★	★★
Press Fasteners	★★★	★	★★	★★

Activity 75

Produce your own chart of fasteners showing how suitable they are to use for people of different ages, for example young children, teenagers and old people.

Buttons

Buttons are one of the most common fastening devices. They come in a wide range of shapes and sizes. They can be sewn directly onto the fabric. Some buttons have stems called **shanks**; others simply have holes through which the thread can pass to stitch the button onto the fabric.

tape
end

top
stop

slider

pusher

teeth

tape

Zips

Zips have become very popular, and often replace buttons. The first zips were made of metal, but modern zips are usually made of nylon. There are three main types of zip:

Open-ended zips, invisible zips and **curved zips.**

Most zips are not seen in textile products.

Zips can be hard to fit. The secret is practice and careful sewing.

Velcro

Velcro is actually many hooks and loops. It is sometimes referred to **as touch-and-close fastening,** because that is all you need to do. It is also called **hook and loop tape.** One side of the Velcro has a large number of fine hooks; the other has a number of fine loops. When they are pressed together, they produce a strong fastening. Touch-and-close fastenings are ideal for children's clothes.

Hook and eye

Hook and eye fasteners are one of the simplest forms of fastening. They are often used together with zips to prevent the zip coming undone. Hooks and eyes come in a variety of colours.

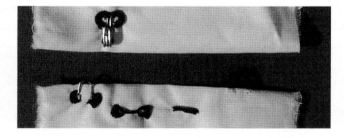

Frog and toggle

Frog and toggle fasteners work in a similar way to buttons. This type of fastener is popular on coats.

end
stop

Press fasteners or studs

Press fasteners work by snapping together. They come in a wide variety of sizes and can be made from plastics and metals. You should only use press studs where there will be little strain. Normally the socket side of the press stud is sewn on the underside of the opening.

Decorative press studs are much stronger. They are usually hammered into position. You can only use them on strong fabric.

Press stud tapes are also available. They have fasteners already fixed at regular intervals along the tape.

Homework

Make a list of at least 12 objects in the home that use temporary fastenings. State the purpose of each fastening and say what alternatives could have been used.

Make a list of each type of fastening mentioned in the book. List two objects in the home that use each type of temporary fastening. State the properties of each fastening and say what alternatives could have been used.

Make a list of each fastening mentioned in the book. List two objects in the home that use each type of temporary fastening. State the properties of each fastening and say what alternatives could have been used and why.

Activity 76

Design and make a pencil case. Look at a number of fabric pencil cases first to get design ideas. Remember to use a paper pattern first. You will need to use permanent and temporary fastenings.

Bags, wallets and purses use both temporary and permanent fastenings. Design a fashion bag, wallet or purse for a 13-year-old based on the theme 'animals'. You must design your own pattern first.

Bags utilise both temporary and permanent fastenings, tucks, pleats and gathering. Design a fashion bag incorporating these techniques. Think about openings and decoration. Your bag should reflect a cultural theme.

Designing Hats

For centuries hats have been an important status symbol. They have been used as religious symbols and to show nationality and wealth. They are also used to protect the wearer from the weather, as part of uniforms and as a fashion accessory.

Hats should be chosen to suit your face. Low hats suit narrow faces, big hats suit round faces and tilted hats suit square faces.

Activity 77

Collect pictures or drawings of a range of different hats. State the main purpose of the hat and say whether you think it meets this purpose effectively. How could you improve the design of the hat for its intended purpose?

Collect pictures or drawings of a range of different hats. State the main purpose of the hat and say whether you think it meets this purpose effectively. How could you improve the design of the hat for its intended purpose? Draw the following hats: turban, cap, panama, trilby. State when they may be worn.

Collect pictures or drawings of a range of different hats. State the main purpose of the hat and say whether you think it meets this purpose effectively. How could you improve the design of the hat for its intended purpose? Find out about the following hats: beret, pillbox, cap and top hat. Draw each hat and state when each would be used. Select two hats and say how you think they have been made.

Making hats

The people who make hats are called **milliners**. Most hats are made using basic sewing skills. Knitting makes the simplest hats. Bobble and pocket hats are both made by knitting.

Other hats are made using a range of construction techniques. Wire, fabric and glue are essential in hat-making.

Hats are designed by using paper patterns. You can make a paper hat and try it out before using fabric. Most hats are made by using simple segment patterns stitched together. Castle hats are made with hexagonal pieces; baseball caps with pieces shaped as shown below.

Designs are often put onto hats using computer-aided manufacture. You could use the school's sewing machine to add a logo to a hat.

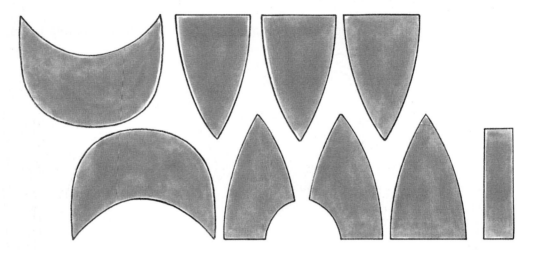

Felt hats

Felt hats are easy to make. The Egyptians made felt hats. They are popular in Iran and Pakistan.

The technique involves pressing wool fibres together around a **former** (like a mould) and then sprinkling it with warm water mixed with washing-up liquid. The felt is then rolled around the former and the friction causes the wool to felt. Alternatively, the felt can be made first using a rolling action and then shaped around the former before being left to dry.

Activity 78

Design a simple baseball cap. Make a paper model first to check the size and shape of your hat. Add a simple decoration to your hat.

Using felt or cloth, design and make a simple hat based on the theme 'seasons'. Add decoration to your hat.

Create an interesting hat or visor using a mixture of felt, wire and traditional construction techniques. Your hat or visor should be designed to reflect a cultural theme. It is to be worn at a wedding or in battle.

The Manufacturing Process

In the different sections of this book you have found out how textile products are made, starting with the raw materials called fibres. In this section you will put all this knowledge together and look at how the everyday textile products that you wear were manufactured.

Most of the textile products we buy today are produced in large numbers. The correct term for this is **mass produced**. Mass-produced textile products are usually cheaper than handmade products. Whilst the methods used to make both handmade products and mass-produced products are similar, computers are used extensively in mass-production methods. The making processes are called the **stages of production**. The stages outlined in this section of the book also explore the important role computers play in modern textile manufacturing.

Raw material
The raw material for textile products comes from natural or manufactured fibres.

polyester   cotton

Spinning
Fibres are made into yarn by spinning.

yarn

Blending
Spun yarn is often blended to produce yarn or fabric with enhanced properties.

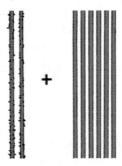

25% cotton   75% polyester

Dyeing
The yarn is often coloured by dye at this point in the manufacturing process, although sometimes the dyeing process is carried out once the material or garment has been produced, or even on the raw fibres before they are spun into yarn.

Weaving

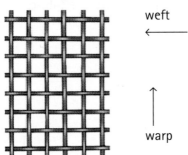

weft
←

↑
warp

Printing
The fabric may at this stage be printed. Fabric can be printed by hand or by machine.

Finishing
The fabric is often coated or treated to **enhance** its properties.

Designing
Designers design the textile product. Today, designers often use Computer-Aided Design to help them to achieve a quality product.

For more on weaving see pages 31–33.
For more on finishing see pages 45–46.

Lay planning

When manufacturers cut out the pieces to make a textile product, they want to ensure there is no waste. The process of working out how best to lay out the pattern pieces is called lay planning. Fabric is sold in different widths. During lay planning, the best width of fabric for the job is also decided. Lay planning was traditionally done by hand. You can work out a lay plan using graph paper and pattern pieces made smaller but to the correct scale. Today, mass-produced textile products are lay planned by using a computer.

Marking out

The design is turned into a pattern which is pinned or drawn onto the fabric.

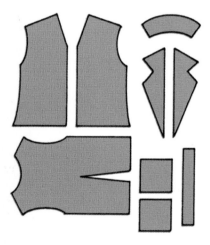

Cutting out the pieces

Traditionally, pattern pieces are cut out by hand using shears. Manufacturers use computer-controlled cutters which can cut through a number of layers of fabric at the same time.

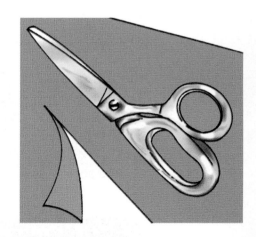

Sewing

The fabric pieces are sewn together. They can be sewn by hand or by human or computer-controlled sewing machines.

Adding trimmings and fastenings

Trimming and fastenings are added to the textile product. Care labels are also added at this stage.

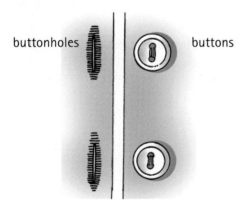

buttonholes   buttons

Pressing

The textile product is pressed to ensure it retains its shape. Pressing is usually done by hand, but some modern presses are computer controlled.

Quality Control

Throughout the making process, manufacturers check the quality of the product. The checking points are called **quality control points**. The process of checking the quality of a product throughout the manufacturing process is called **quality assurance**. Let us explore the type of checks that could be carried out during the process outlined above.

Process	Check	Action
1 Cut fabric	check for flaws	avoid flaws
2 Assembly	check stitch lengths check pattern pieces to ensure correct sides are together	adjust machines check before machining

Packaging

The textile product is packed ready for despatch to the shops. Textile items can be packed manually or using computer-controlled machines.

Selling

The textile product is sold to the customer. Computers are often used to help the shopkeeper control stock levels. They are also used at the checkouts.

Activity 79

Draw a flow chart to show how raw fibres end up in the shops as textile products.

Draw a flow chart using pictures and notes to explain how raw wool fibres are converted into the products we buy from the shops.

Draw a flow chart using pictures and notes to explain how raw cotton fibres are converted into the products we buy from the shops. Identify quality control points throughout your process and state what checks need to be done and why.

Costs

Costing the manufacturing process is a very important part of the production of textile products. If you make a mistake when you are working out the cost of making a one-off textile product, and it costs you an extra £4.00, this has no lasting implication. Imagine the implication to a manufacturer of producing 500,000 garments if the same error were made. The company could become bankrupt.

There are a number of costs that need to be taken into account. These are split into **direct** and **indirect** costs.

Direct costs

The cost of the fabric, yarn and accessories and the cost of labour used to make the textile product are called direct costs. Manufacturers also have to consider waste and add this into the direct cost of the product. Any product that is below standard has direct cost implications in terms of the material wasted and the labour and machine costs involved in making it. If the product is below standard at the fabric weaving stage, the manufacturer will not want to pay for it to be made into a finished garment.

The name given to the outputs of the labour force and the machine costs of each stage of manufacture is **value adding**. This is because each stage makes the product worth more money. For example, yarn is more valuable than fibre, fabric more valuable than yarn and the finished garment worth more than the fabric before it is made into anything. You would not go into a shop and buy a ball of wool for the same price as a finished jumper. Manufacturing is all about adding value.

Indirect costs

The cost of buying the equipment that will be used to make a number of textile products and the cost of rent, electricity, heating and lighting are called indirect costs. Other indirect costs include advertising, transport to the shops, the cost of any unsold items, damaged items and storage.

When you work out the cost of your textile products you will probably only count the direct costs like the material and fastenings. Your school and parents will have provided the equipment, electricity, heat and space. Although you have not had to pay for these, they do have a cost, and if you were producing textile products for sale, you would need to take account of this cost.

Test

1. What is anthropometrics and why is it important?
2. What is the difference between frame and shell structures?
3. Why are paper patterns important in textile design?
4. What are the two ways of joining fabric together? Explain the main methods of each.
5. Explain, using illustrations, two of the following: flat seam, piped seam, French seam, overlaid seam, seam and fell.
6. Describe two finishes used on the edges of textile products.
7. What is a pleat; what is a tuck; where are they used?
8. How are felt hats produced and where are they still popular?
9. Describe the manufacturing process of a textile product from raw material to sale.
10. What are the differences between direct and indirect costs?

Glossary

Abrasive	A substance used to remove matter by scratching and grinding.
Adorn	Decorate
Anthropometrics	Measuring the human body, usually to obtain the best 'fit' of tools and equipment.
Appliqué	The art of sewing patches of fabric onto a textile item to decorate it. The patches are usually sewn on with embroidery stitches.
Bain-marie	A pot containing simmering water. A vessel containing a substance (normally a food item, or wax) is set inside the bain-marie and the gentle heat of the water melts the contents of the vessel.
Bandhani	The name for tie and dye fabrics in some parts of India.
Basket weave	A type of weave that produces softer fabrics than plain weave. It is sometimes called hopsack weave.
Batik	A method of colouring fabric by creating a physical barrier, commonly wax, between the dye and the fabric.
Bias	Diagonal to the warp and weft of fabric. Fabric is sometimes cut 'on the bias' to achieve stretch.
Binder	A substance used to hold two or more other substances in a stable mixture.
Binding	Strip of fabric, normally cut on the bias, used to edge textile products. It may be used for decorative purposes, or to add strength and finish edges.
Blending	Mixing two or more media together; in textiles, mixing fibres together to achieve the best properties in the yarn.
Block printing	Applying colour and design to a fabric by stamping it with a coloured block bearing a design. The block may be made of material such as wood, lino, cork, sponge or potato.
Bobbin	Thread carrier in the body of a sewing machine.

Bodice	Fitted part of a female garment that covers the upper torso (excluding the arms).
Bonding	Joining two or more media together so that they become one.
Bouclé	Two yarns twisted together, with one of the yarns kept slack to give a distinctive appearance and feel.
Braiding	Decorating with braid, a type of ornate ribbon. *Also*, plaiting.
Brick stitch	An embroidery stitch where the pattern created looks like bricks.
Bulk	Mass
CAD	Computer Aided Design
CAM	Computer Aided Manufacture
Carbon paper	Paper with a special backing that is used to make duplicate copies. A normal sheet of paper is written, typed or drawn on, with carbon paper beneath it and a second sheet of paper beneath that. The backing comes off the carbon paper as a transfer on the second sheet.
Cartoon	A specific design for a fabric.
Casting on	The process of making the first row of stitches when knitting.
Casting off	The process of making the final row of stitches when knitting.
Cellulose fibre	Natural fibre made from plants.
Chain stitch	A common embroidery stitch where the pattern created looks like a chain.
CNC	Computer Numeric Control (for example, on a milling machine)
Colour relationship	The effect of colours upon other colours – how they look when placed next to each other.
Colourfast	Where the dye in a fabric will not run when the fabric is washed.
Complementary	Where two colours, when placed next to each other, or close together, enhance each other.
Contrasting	Where two colours, when placed next to each other, or close together, are so different that a startling effect is created.

Conversion	Changing the state of something; in textiles, the process of turning fibres into yarns.
Cord	Yarns twisted together to create special effects.
Crackling	A method of colouring fabric where the fabric is coated with wax, which is then allowed to crack, allowing dye to reach the fabric.
Crimping	Pressing into folds or bending into shape.
Crochet	Creating a textile product by using a crochet hook to make a design of stitches.
Cross stitch	A very common embroidery stitch in the form of crosses.
Darts	Methods of adjusting fabric fullness at seam lines and in the body of garments.
Dévoré	A process where acid or chemicals are used to dissolve away areas of fabric, to achieve an effect like lace.
Direct costs	The costs immediately involved in the manufacture of a product: raw materials and labour.
Discord	Lack of harmony; where two or more media 'fight' each other.
Distorting	*In textiles*, treating manufactured fibres with heat, which changes their shape to produce three dimensional textures.
Drape	The way a fabric hangs.
Dry cleaning	Cleaning textiles by using chemicals, without water and detergent.
Dye	A substance used to colour fabric. The dye may be natural or manufactured.
Embossed	Decorated with a raised design.
Ergonomics	The science of designing machines, tools and equipment so that they 'fit' the needs of users. For example, shaping the handle of a tool so that it fits the human hand in the best way possible.
Etched	Where a design has eaten into a fabric.
Fabric	Textile made by weaving yarn. Before being made into a textile item, fabric is normally stored in rolls.

Facing	Panels of fabric applied to the inside of a garment or other textile item to finish and strengthen edges.
Felt	A dense fabric created by layering fibres, usually of wool, with each layer at right angles to that below it. The layers are then washed and, as they dry, they shrink and mat together.
Fibre	Raw material used to make textile products. Fibre may be natural or manufactured.
Filament fibre	Continuous length of fibre, usually manufactured fibre. The only natural filament fibre is silk.
Fix	To make a dye stable so that it will not run in a fabric.
Flocking	A method of creating a particular raised, patterned fabric texture, usually by adding glue to fabric and then adding fine flocking fibres to the glue.
Folk embroidery	Embroidery traditionally done by ordinary people to decorate everyday items.
Former	A device to shape hats or three dimensional textile products.
Frame structure	A structure that gains its strength from a number of strips which make up a frame.
French seam	A strong seam traditionally used for transparent fabrics and fine fabrics that are likely to fray. The two pieces of fabric are first sewn together with wrong sides together, the resulting seam is trimmed and then the fabric is turned right sides together and stitched so that the first seam is concealed inside and there are no raw edges.
Frog and toggle	A fastening method traditionally used on outerwear such as duffel coats.
Function	What something does.
Garland	A design in the form of a ring, or curves, of flowers or plants.
Gathers	A method of adjusting fullness in a textile item, typically where a sleeve is set in the armhole of a garment, or a full skirt is attached to a fitted waistband. A gathering thread is run through the fuller fabric and then gently drawn up until the length of the fabric matches the part to which it is to be joined.

Gin	A machine that separates cotton fibre from cotton seeds.
Goblin stitch	An embroidery stitch similar to cross stitch.
Grain	The way the pile of a fabric lies.
Greater embroidery	Fine, high quality embroidery, traditionally of items for use in the church, or for very important people such as royalty.
Gutta	A gum that can be painted directly onto fabric as an alternative to wax when dying.
Harmony	When two colours or effects blend together to good effect.
Hooking	Pulling fibres, threads, yarns or pieces of fabric through another fabric.
Hopsack	A type of weave that produces softer fabrics than plain weave. It is sometimes known as basket weave.
Hue	Correct name for the range of colours available for textile products.
Indirect costs	All of the costs involved in the manufacture of a product, excluding direct costs: cost of building, heat, light, administration, etc.
Intensity	The strength, depth of a colour.
Jacquard	A type of loom that allows the creation of complicated designs during the weaving process. Jacquard looms are normally computer controlled.
Kembanagan	A name for tie and dye in Indonesia.
Keratin	An animal protein found in natural fibres that have come from animal sources. Silk and wool are examples.
Knit	A process of producing a textile fabric by using hand knitting needles or a knitting machine to stitch thread, often wool, into fabric.
Laminating	Joining two or more layers of fabric together with glue or stitching to make one fabric.
Lay planning	The process of deciding how best to lay pattern pieces on fabric in order to make the best use of the fabric available.
Loop	A loose thread in a yarn or fabric.

Marbling	A form of dying where fabric is crumpled into a ball and the ball is bound with thread. The finished effect on the fabric looks like marble.
Mass produced	Items produced in large quantities, normally in a factory setting.
Mengikat	Malaysian term meaning to tie.
Microfibre	A fibre that is extremely fine, developed by technologists for use in new fabrics.
Milliner	A person who makes and decorates hats.
Minerals	Natural substances, neither animal nor vegetable, that come from the Earth's crust. Certain minerals can be ground up to make natural dyes.
Mixing	*In textiles*, combining yarns.
Mohair	A soft cloth made from the fine hair of the Angora goat.
Mordant	A substance used to fix colour in a fabric. Salt is a common mordant for cotton and linen; vinegar is a common mordant for wool and silk.
Moulding (as in felt)	Shaping a fabric like felt around a mould in order to make a textile item such as a hat.
Nap	The 'woolly' surface on a fabric. This may be raised in a finishing process.
Natural dyes	Substances derived from natural products such as berries, flowers, leaves, bark and some minerals and used to colour fabrics.
Notch and clip	A way of trimming excess fabric from a seam by making small cuts into the fabric and trimming it away. This will help the seam to lie flat.
Nub	*In textiles*, yarn with a distinctive shape made by introducing lumps of yarn at regular intervals.
Nylon	The first synthetic fibre (made from chemicals), invented in 1935.
Optical illusion	Something that, when looked at, appears to be something it is not.
Ornament	Decoration.
Overlaid seam	A seam used on gathered, pleated or tucked fabric, made by folding the fabric or inserting a piece of different fabric.

Overlocker	A sewing machine used to cover the edges of a textile product with a locked stitch. The machine has up to four top threads but no bobbins for the lower thread. Instead, loopers form the loops that allow the finished stitch to stretch with the stretch of the fabric.
Part-textile material	A modern fabric that has been made by combining textile with a substance such as metal or glass, for special effect.
Photosensitive	Reacting to light.
Pigments	Minerals that have been ground up to be used as dyes.
Pile	The raised surface of a fabric, made during the weaving process.
Pinking shears	Scissors with serrated edges that cut fabric in zig-zag lines, helping to prevent fraying.
Piped seam	A seam finished with what looks like a pipe along it. It is a popular decoration technique on many textile items such as upholstered chairs and car seats. The pipe can be made with the fabric being used for the body of the textile item, or with a contrasting fabric, and it may be stiffened with cord inside it.
Pleats	Methods of folding and sewing fabric in textile items such as clothing to achieve fit, with freedom of movement.
Plies	Strands of yarn produced by spinning.
Primary colour	One of the three basic hues, red, yellow or blue, from which all other colours are made up.
Prodding	*In textiles*, pushing fibres or fabrics together, usually with a sharp tool.
Protein fibre	A fibre such as silk or wool, from an animal source, usually composed of the protein keratin.
Puff pigment	A rubber or other expanding pigment that can be added to a fabric to achieve puckering and distorting.
Purl	A knitting stitch, combining plain and rib stitches and used to give lengthwise and crosswise stretch.
Quality assurance	The maintenance of quality in all aspects of a manufacturing environment.
Quality control	A process of checking and sampling quality of work in progress at marked points in a manufacturing process.

Quilting	Layers of fabric joined together by sewing, often with a layer of padding sandwiched between two outer layers to achieve warmth.
Ragwork	A traditional craft that uses fibres and rags from old textile items to make new ones.
Ratine	A yarn with distinctive texture made by winding an outer yarn around a core yarn.
Regenerated fibre	Manufactured fibre created from waste products.
Relief printing	A method of printing fabrics, like block printing. A waterproof adhesive is used to stick string or thread onto a printing block, often made of thick card. The raised string or thread makes the design.
Resin	Substance obtained from the sap of certain plants and trees – natural resin. Synthetic resin may be manufactured by chemical processes.
Resist	*In textiles*, a method where a medium such as wax is applied to a fabric before it is dyed, to create a particular effect when the dye is applied.
Rhythm	*In textiles*, regular pattern repeats on a fabric.
Rib	A method of knitting that uses two sets of needles to allow greater variety in fabric design and greater elasticity widthways. *Also*, a weave where fine and coarse yarns are alternated to produce a ribbed effect.
Richelieu cut work	A form of fabric decoration where fine linen is embroidered with button hole stitches and then cut away.
Roller printing	A method of printing fabric where the design is etched onto copper rollers. The rollers pick up colour from a dye bath and transfer it onto the fabric.
S twist	Cotton twisted in a clockwise direction during spinning.
Satin	A closely woven silk with a shiny surface that shows much of the warp.
Screen printing	A versatile method of printing fabric. A stencil is placed beneath or on top of a meshed fabric, over the fabric to be printed. Colour is then pressed through the mesh and all areas are printed except those protected by the stencil.

Seam and fell	A type of seam used to give strength. Two pieces of fabric are first seamed with wrong sides together. One side of the seamed edge is then trimmed back and the wider edge folded, pressed and stitched over it. This type of seam is also known as a machine fell seam.
Secondary colour	One of the colours orange, green or purple that is made by mixing together any two of the primary colours.
Selvage	The edge of a fabric where the weft thread turns. The selvage does not fray because there are no loose ends.
Serrated	Notched like a saw, with sharp, forward-pointing 'teeth'.
Shade	Any colour with black added to it to alter it.
Shanks	Stems on some buttons.
Shears	Scissors designed for cutting fabrics.
Shell structure	A structure that gets its strength from its own shape in a similar way to natural shells.
Shibori	Japanese term for tie and dye.
Sinew	Animal tendons that join muscle to bone, used as early thread.
Slub	Yarn with an irregular thickness, made by adding extra tufts of fibre or by loosening the twist.
Smyrna stitch	An embroidery stitch similar to cross stitch.
Soumak weaving	A traditional weave commonly used to make rugs.
Spinning	The process of twisting fibres together to make continuous yarn. Spinning can be done by hand or by machine.
Staple fibre	Another name for natural fibre.
Stencil	A cut-out shape used to control the application of colour to a fabric to create designs. The stencil prevents colour from reaching certain areas of the fabric.
Structure	How something is made.
Synthetic fibre	Manufactured fibre made from chemicals obtained from coal or petroleum.

Tactile texture	The interesting 'feel' of a surface.
Tertiary colour	A colour created by mixing a primary colour with a secondary colour.
Textile	Any product that is made from fabric.
Texturising	Using a process to add texture.
Tint	Any colour with white added to it to alter it.
Tjanting	Special tool used to apply wax for batik work.
Tjap	A printing block, or stamp, used to apply wax for batik.
Transfer printing	An industrial method of printing large volumes of fabric. The design is printed first onto a roll of paper and heat and pressure are then used to transfer the image from the paper onto the fabric.
Triaxial interlocking weave	A type of weave that has three interlocks rather than the usual two (warp and weft).
Tritik	A form of dying fabric that uses stitches, rather than tied thread or wax to resist dye.
Tucks	Folds in fabric, held in place with stitching, used to shape and decorate textile items.
Tufted quilting	The simplest type of quilting, where one or more strands of thread are taken through the fabric layers twice and tied in knots at regular intervals.
Twill (weave)	A type of weave that typically shows diagonal ridges across the fabric, either from left to right or right to left. This is achieved by weft threads passing over two warp threads, then under two warp threads in an organised stepped pattern. Twill weave is used to increase bulk and, therefore, warmth.
Value (as in colour)	The lightness or darkness of any colour. Value can be changed by adding black or white.
Vertical interlocking	A term used in weaving to achieve a change in colour part way across the warp by interlocking the old and new colours.
Viscose rayon	A regenerated fibre made from cellulose from wood, and wool. Viscose rayon may be used as a substitute for silk, being less expensive.

Visual texture	How a fabric appears to feel.
Warp	Thread running vertically (top to bottom) on a loom.
Warp knitting	A relatively modern method of knitting where hundreds, sometimes thousands, of yarns are inter-looped vertically into adjacent yarns to make a flat fabric with straight edges.
Weave	To interlock warp and weft yarns on a loom to form a fabric.
Weft	Threads running horizontally (left to right to left) on a loom.
Weft knitting	The common form of hand knitting where a single yarn travels horizontally to make a row of loops into which the following row of loops can be knitted.
Wrapping	A technique used in ragwork.
Yarn	Strand of textile thread produced by spinning fibres.
Z twist	Cotton twisted in an anti-clockwise direction during spinning.

Index

Pearson Education Limited
Edinburgh Gate
Harlow
Essex, CM20 2JE
England

Second impression 2002
ISBN 0582 34437 9

Designed by Moondisks, Cambridge.

Cover photography by Gareth Boden, Sawbridgeworth.

Printed in China
SWTC/02

Acknowledgements:

The author wishes to thank Jill Bury and the pupils of St Paul's School, Milton Keynes, for their help.

The publisher wishes to thank Gill Langan and Presdales School, Ware, Hertfordshire for their kind assistance in the production of the front cover photographs.

We are grateful to the following for permission to reproduce photographs:

Ancient Egypt Picture Library, page 95 (Bob Partridge); Art Directors & TRIP, page 71 *centre right* (Eric Smith); Camera Press, pages 60 (Ben Coster), 60/61 (Wattie Cheung) 61 (Ben Coster); Gerber Technology, page 16; Rex Features, page 23; Science Photo Library, pages 15 (James King-Holmes), 19 *left*, 20 *top left* (Eye of Science), 20 *top right*, 20 *bottom*, 33 (NASA), 71 *centre left* (Pascal Goetgheluck), 71 *right* (Adam Hart-Davis); Stone, pages 19 *right* (Andrew Syred), 71 *left* (Laurie Campbell).